D1106654

GALLS and GALL INSECTS

GALLS and GALL INSECTS

ROSS E. HUTCHINS

Illustrated with photographs by the author

DODD, MEAD & COMPANY, NEW YORK

To Jo and Jim Cliatt
in appreciation of their help

CONTENTS

INTRODUCTION

The world of nature is filled with many remarkable things. In order to see these wonders, many people believe that they must travel to far places. As a naturalist, I have often journeyed long distances to study and photograph some unusual plant or animal. Yet, I am sure that I could usually have found equally fascinating things near my home. Many of the world's most astonishing plants and animals can be discovered in almost any back yard or in nearby forests and fields.

No doubt in some of your ramblings afield you have noticed small, fruit-like growths on twigs and leaves. Probably you gave these only passing glances and walked on, looking for other things. What you saw and failed to investigate were plant galls, usually caused by insects. In some remarkable, but little understood way, these insects stimulate the plants to create them. In a manner of speaking, they are grown to order for the insects and furnish them with everything they need, including plentiful food supplies and protection from enemies.

Plant galls are almost endless in form, coloration, and size, and many of the insects that produce them have habits and life histories that are truly "stranger than fiction."

This is the story of the gall-forming insects and of the strange plant growths they create. You will find them almost everywhere, in forests, fields, and even in city parks.

—R. E. H.

7

Plant galls created by insects, mites, and fungi, are of many shapes and sizes and may be found on almost all parts of trees and plants.

I

WHAT IS A PLANT GALL?

Insects do many remarkable things but their ability to force plants to grow dwelling places, stocked with food, for them can certainly be rated among their more unusual accomplishments. Many kinds of insects, perhaps most, feed upon plants but the majority merely eat the leaves and other parts, making no changes in the plants except for the damage they cause. There are, however, a large number of insects, as well as certain mites, that not only feed upon plants but cause the plants to produce special structures within which they live and feed.

An oak leaf is flat and blade-like with toothed or undulating margins. This is its normal form. If, however, we examine a number of oak leaves, especially in spring and early summer, we are apt to discover that to some of them are attached marble-like spheres, often an inch or more in diameter, or other peculiar structures. If we cut one of these spherical "galls" open we find it to be filled with fibers, all radiating outward to its walls from a hard, central core. It is quite an elaborate structure and

Oak-apple galls are formed on twigs, leaves or, as shown here, on the leaf buds. (Life size: 1 inch in diameter)

it is difficult to believe that it is not something that the plant has produced in the normal course of its growth. If the central core is cut open, we find that it contains a small white grub. This grub is the larval form of a tiny wasp and it was the wasp that caused the leaf to produce the spherical growth in the first place. In effect, the grub caused the oak not only to grow a home within which it could live in safety from most enemies but surrounded with abundant food. No insect could ask for better cooperation from a plant. The plant, of course, is not benefited; in fact, if there are many galls the tree or plant may be seriously injured. The plant is, thus, actually an unwilling cooperator in the arrangement.

Plant galls have been defined as being "abnormal growths of plant tissues produced by a stimulus external to the plant it-

10

self." This stimulus may result from mere mechanical irritation or from some chemical substance secreted by the insect. It is truly remarkable that each kind of gall-forming insect produces its own special kind of gall. Since most gall insects are small and live inside the structures they create, they are much less well known than the strange and unusual growths they produce. Some plant galls are as large as baseballs while their insect creators are very minute. As Robert Browning once said, "We find great things are made of little things." With regard to galls, we can say with truth, that great galls are made by tiny insects. People have seen and been mystified by plant galls for several thousand years but not until recent times have they known much about them.

Even though the true origin of galls remained unknown for

Oak-apples are created by the larvae of small wasps of the family Cynipidae. Such galls arise as a result of growth-stimulating substances secreted by the gall insect larvae. (Life size of wasp: 1/16 inch long)

many centuries, they were often used as sources of tannin and other substances. Tannin has a very bitter taste and the fact that most oak galls contain large amounts of it was no doubt the reason that they, long ago, became known as "galls." They tasted as bitter as gall and so were called gallnuts. That branch of science dealing with the plant galls is called *cecidology*, a term of Greek origin meaning "the study of gallnuts." A gall is called a *cecidium* and an insect-produced gall is known as an *entocecidium* (plural: *entocecidia*).

Insects are, of course, not the only living animals that produce plant galls. There are a number of mites, close relatives of spiders, that cause gall formation on a wide variety of plants. In addition, a number of galls are produced on plants by fungi. We often find large, ball-like growths on the twigs of cedar trees. These galls are caused by one stage in the life cycle of a fungus, the same fungus that produces abnormal spots on apple leaves. On apple trees, the disease is known as cedar-apple rust

Some tree galls mature in autumn and fall to the ground. The winged wasps do not emerge until the next spring, or sometimes not until several years later.

When mature, this large oak gall is filled with dried fibers among which are the cells of the gall-making wasp larvae. Some galls have very thick walls while others, such as this one, have quite thin walls.

because the infective fungus spores are blown by winds to the apple trees from nearby cedar trees. There are numerous other kinds of plant galls, each created by a certain insect, mite, nematode (microscopic worm), or fungus. Some plant galls are produced by bacteria and viruses.

Thus, there are other agencies besides insects that cause the growth of plant galls. In each case there is a scientific term relating to the cause of the gall. A gall produced by a fungus is called a *mycetocecidium*, one produced by a mite is called an *acarocecidium*, while a *helminthocecidium* is a gall created by a microscopic worm or nematode. In this book we will be concerned mostly with galls produced by insects such as gall wasps, gall gnats, and others.

13

Plant galls are of almost every conceivable form and coloration. Their shapes range from spheres to tubes, and from those with smooth surfaces to those covered with spines. In size, they range from very minute to oak-apple galls two inches in diameter. Since ancient times, people have noticed these strange, abnormal plant growths and many kinds are so common that they have been designated by popular names. Some attractive galls found on rose leaves are known as "robins' pincushions." In the Near East, similar galls are known as "bedeguar" galls. The word *bedeguar* is, seemingly, derived from the Arabic *badawar* meaning "wind-brought," or, perhaps, compounded from the Persian *bād*, meaning "wind," and the Arabic word *ward*, meaning "rose." Thus, the word might be interpreted as meaning "wind rose." In any case, we have here a definite indication that ancient people had no idea as to what actually caused the formation of plant galls.

For some but little understood reason, certain plant groups are more attractive to gall producers than others. Possibly this is because these plants respond more readily to the gall-producing substances they secrete. Oak trees are favored by a large variety of gall-producing insects, while the lower plants, such as ferns, mosses, fungi, and algae, are rarely infested. Yet there are seven kinds of flies that create galls on mushrooms, one or two galls appear on lichens (produced by mites), and several galls grow on algae (produced by nematodes or microscopic worms). Apparently, as plants have advanced up the evolutionary ladder, they have shown an increasing tendency to become hosts to gall formers. The ferns, for instance, are higher on the ladder than the algae, fungi, and mosses and there are about a dozen different kinds of galls found on them, most of which are caused by insects. Below the ferns, there are few plants infested by gall-forming insects.

In many cases, gall-making insects leave the galls while they are still attached to the twigs, leaves or stems. Here, the adult gall wasp has emerged through a round exit hole.

It becomes evident that the flowering plants harbor most of the gall makers, most of which are associated with only eleven plant families. Below are listed these plant families and the number of different insect and mite galls found on them in North America:

Oak family	805	Mint family	16
Daisy family	181	Snapdragon family	8
Rose family	133	Madder family	5
Willow family	114	Mustard family	3
Grass family	68	Parsley family	3
Pea family	32		

Goldenrod galls are found almost everywhere that these plants grow. Protected by the thick walls of the galls, the larvae of a gall fly (Eurosta) *feed upon the nutritious plant tissues.*

Almost every insect group has gall-producing members, but most galls are produced by either gall wasps of the family Cynipidae, or by gall gnats or midges of the family Cecidomyiidae. Of the 2,000 gall-producing insects in the United States, 1,500 are either gall wasps or gall gnats. Of all plants and trees, the oaks are the favorite hosts of these insects.

Paleontologists, those who study ancient plants and animals, have discovered that gall-forming insects are of quite ancient

16

origin. They were apparently not as abundant in the ancient forests as at present. However, fossil galls on leaves have been found in Tertiary formations laid down about fifty million years ago. Large numbers of galls occur on leaves from the Cretaceous Period, that time in the distant past when the flowering plants were just appearing. This was more than a hundred million years ago. What kinds of insects produced these ancient galls is unknown, but two gall wasps have been found in Baltic amber from lower Oligocene time (about thirty-six million years old). A gall wasp was also discovered in a piece of Cretaceous amber found in Canada. Apparently, none of these early gall producers infested oaks. Thus, it seems evident that gall wasps' preference for oaks is of recent origin, geologically speaking.

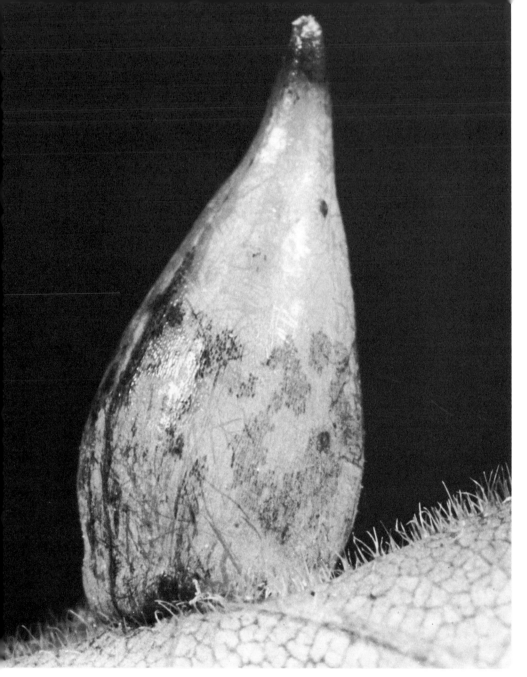

Galls of many kinds are produced by midge flies, sometimes called gall gnats. This seed gall on a hickory leaf resulted from stimulating substances secreted by the larval fly (Caryomyia) living inside. (Life size: 1/4 inch tall)

2

HOW PLANT GALLS ARE PRODUCED

Plant galls are very remarkable things in several respects; they resemble some sort of seed-bearing fruit but are not fruit at all. Instead, they are created by the presence of an insect, mite, or fungus but, like fruit, they usually contain abundant food and so are highly nutritious. What is especially remarkable is that each kind of gall is created by a certain kind of gall maker and many of the galls they create have very complex structures and may be quite colorful and attractive. On the leaves of certain oaks there frequently appear galls resembling small vases covered with reddish or yellowish spines. These, known as spiny vase galls, are created by a tiny gall wasp (*Xanthoteras*). They are very characteristic and one need not actually see the wasp to know its identification.

If we study one of these pretty galls under a hand lens we find it to be even more interesting than when viewed without magnification. It is, indeed, difficult to believe that it was not produced by the oak leaf in the course of its normal growth. How, you might ask, can an insect cause the oak to create such a special structure, so perfectly fitted to serve as its dwelling place? And how is it that the galls created by each kind of gall insect are identical in form and coloration? In short, what is the gall-making insects' secret?

I wish I could tell you that it has now been discovered that gall-making insects inject a complex chemical substance into the plants, causing them to create the special growths we call galls and that chemists have analyzed and identified the chemicals that the insects inject. Unfortunately, this is not the case; biologists know very little more about plant gall formation than they did a hundred years ago. As long ago as 1686, Marcello Malpighi, an Italian scientist, suggested that plant galls were created by some sort of "fly" and, even though his investigations failed to reveal the actual insects involved, his observations were quite accurate. He wrote:

> Thus, the very fertile family of flies emerging from the galls follow the dictates of Nature to wound and perforate the soft parts of plants with the file-like ovipositor. Then in accordance with their diverse nature and relations, tumors of similarly varied kinds arise. The liquid arising from the ovipositor is highly active and fermentative, and when injected, this excites a new fermentation or internal motion within the delicate, growing particles of the plant. The nutritive sap accumulated in the transverse vessels begins to ferment and swell when acted upon by the moving air, just as we ourselves and certain of the perfected sanguineous animals react to the wound inflicted by bees immediately after their secretion has been introduced.

Malpighi, it seemed, believed that plant galls resulted from a

Spiny-vase galls, found on the leaves of certain oaks, are produced by gall wasps (Xanthoteras) *and are complex structures. (Life size: 1/4 inch tall)*

"stinging" of the plant by an insect with a resulting swelling of the tissues such as occurs when a person is stung by a bee. This, of course, is not exactly true, yet he did realize that these abnormal growths arose as a result of attacks by insects.

Four theories regarding gall production have been suggested: (1) that the insects inject a special chemical into the plants at the time they lay their eggs in it, (2) that the galls result from mere mechanical irritation caused by the presence of the insect

21

larvae as they burrow through the tissues of the plants, (3) that the galls result from a saliva secreted by the insect larvae, and (4) that waste materials from the insects' bodies are responsible for the growth of the galls.

During recent years, a number of scientists have investigated the matter of gall formation and discovered a good many facts, yet we still do not know exactly how galls are created. Evidently, they do not always result from substances injected by the parent insect at the time she lays her eggs on or in the plants. Some gall-making insects lay their eggs on leaves and, after hatching, the young crawl to another location before actually boring into the plant to begin feeding. Thus, the gall may be produced some distance from the egg-laying site.

In some insects, the female does inject a gall-producing material into the plant at the time she deposits her egg but if the egg does not hatch, the typical gall fails to develop fully. Evidently, the larvae, after hatching, continue to secrete the same substance, causing the gall to complete its growth.

In 1881 it was first definitely proven that gall formation resulted from chemical substances secreted by the insects. Research workers have since been able to create typical galls on plants by injecting them with crushed glands from the bodies of some gall-producing insects. Just what the actual chemical substance is has so far not been established. However, there is evidence that it is related to plant-growth regulators or *auxins*. These auxins have the ability to stimulate the growth of plant cells, resulting in the formation of the galls. It is a fact, too, that galls are produced only on leaves or other plant parts that are actively growing. Thus, galls arise in spring when the plants are commencing to grow. After a leaf is fully developed a gall insect usually cannot cause it to produce a gall because its tissues are no longer capable of active growth.

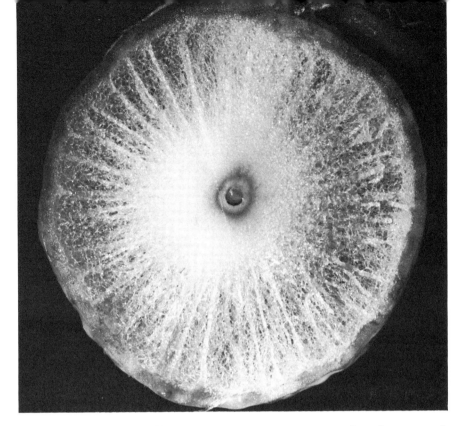

This large oak-apple gall, seen in cross-section, was produced on an oak twig by the larval wasp at the center. (Life size: 1 inch in diameter)

When mature, the larval wasp transforms into a pupa and, eventually, into an adult wasp. After emerging from the gall and mating, the female will lay her eggs in oak twigs, stimulating them to form other galls. (Life size: 1/8 inch long)

Sometimes gall-producing insects lay more than one egg at a time in the same location. This results in a cluster of galls. These red galls with white caps were created on a scarlet oak leaf by a gall wasp. (Life size: 1/8 inch tall)

Gall-making insects, as well as mites, apparently secrete some chemical substance into the plants, stimulating them to create the strange structures we call galls. In effect, the plant is forced to grow a new organ or part, perfectly adapted to shelter and feed its insect—or mite—host. As we have seen, scientists have not yet been able to determine the true nature of the chemical substance secreted by gall-making insects. They have, however, been able to isolate it and to crystallize it and to determine that it is rich in nucleic acid and protein, carbohydrates and other substances. It is especially interesting that it contains nucleic acid, the chemical substance that holds the key to the transfer of hereditary characteristics from one plant—or animal—generation to the next. So it seems probable that the substances injected into plants by the insects actually control the growth and

24

division of the cells, causing them to develop into special structures. In effect, the insects change the genetics of the surrounding cells, forcing them to form themselves into special habitats for the use of the insects.

While we, as yet, do not know the exact composition of the gall-producing chemicals, we do have a name for them; they are called *cecidogens*. I often wonder if we may not one day be able to spray trees or inject them with special chemical sub-

Individual galls often contain several insect larvae as shown in this photograph of a hackberry twig gall created by gall midge flies (Caryomyia). *(Life size: 1/4 inch)*

These thin-walled apple galls that look like fruit were produced on the leaves of an oak tree by gall wasp larvae (Cynips). (Life size: 1 inch in diameter)

stances causing them to grow nutritious "fruit" to order. Such "fruit" could, theoretically, be produced, having the desired content of proteins, carbohydrates, vitamins, minerals, and other things. They would be without seeds and could perhaps be enclosed in hard, protective shells that would keep them in marketable condition for long periods. Such "fruit" could even be created in various colors to please the eye. Farfetched? Perhaps. Yet this, in effect, is what gall-forming insects do. They inject a cecidogen into a plant and the plant responds by creating a new, special "fruit" filled with the proper food and colored according to a predetermined "plan." Remember that each kind of gall insect produces a characteristic gall and that these galls vary but little as to structure and color. Eventually, I believe, chemists will learn the exact chemical structure of the cecidogens and be able to duplicate them in the laboratory. Actually, they have already accomplished many equally remarkable things. Why could not an oak tree be injected with special cecidogens causing them to produce "fruit" having the characteristics of bananas, oranges, or apples? This is more or less what gall-making insects have been doing for millions of years!

Malpighi, long ago, conceived the idea that a plant gall arises in much the same manner as the swellings which usually occur on our bodies when we are stung by wasps or bees. But gall production on plants is much more complicated than this.

As a typical illustration, a tiny gall wasp deposits its egg in the tissues of an oak leaf in the early spring while the leaf cells are still in the process of active growth. Until the egg hatches there is no swelling or distortion of the leaf. When, however, the egg hatches and the young larval wasp begins feeding and secreting its gall-forming substances, the surrounding plant cells begin to grow in an abnormal fashion, slowly forming the strange enlargement we call a gall. These galls, as we have already seen, have characteristic forms according to the kinds of insects that produce them. After the formation of the gall has started, the wasp larva begins secreting enzymes that change the starch of the plant's cells into sugar. In some cases, so much sugar is created in this fashion that droplets of sugary honeydew exude from the outer surface of the gall where it is often collected by ants and bees. In the Southwest, honey ants avail themselves of this source of sweets which constitutes their chief food supply. In certain places, honeybees gather and store large quantities of gall honeydew.

27

These cone galls were produced on the upper surfaces of witch-hazel leaves by aphids or plant lice (Hormaphis hamamelidis). In autumn, the winged aphids escape through openings in the lower surfaces of the leaves and pass the next stage in their life cycle on birch trees.

This gall, two inches in diameter, was produced on a cedar tree by a fungus (Gymnosporangium).

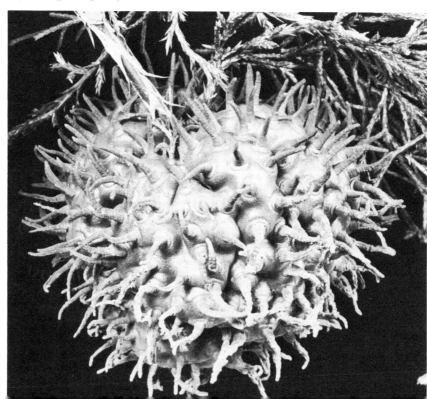

3

LIVES OF THE GALL MAKERS

The life cycles of gall insects are almost as varied as the kinds of insects themselves. In some cases, the insects' life histories are relatively simple; they are but little different from those of ordinary plant-eating kinds. By contrast, the lives of others are extremely complex. Perhaps the best example of one having a simple life history is the goldenrod gall moth.

The female of this small moth lays her eggs on old goldenrod stems in autumn and there they remain until spring when the eggs hatch and the young caterpillars crawl to new, growing goldenrod plants and bore into their stems. At the site where each caterpillar enters the stem an enlargement gradually develops. No doubt this abnormal growth is caused by some substance secreted by the caterpillar as it feeds and grows within the stem.

By midsummer the caterpillar is full grown and the gall within which it lives is spindle-shaped and about half an inch in diameter.

Goldenrod spindle galls are created by caterpillars of a gall moth (Gnorimo-schema). *Left: They bore into young goldenrods where they cause the stems to enlarge. Right: When full grown, the caterpillar cuts an opening in the wall of the gall, sealing it with silk.*

The caterpillar is now ready to transform into its pupal or resting stage, but before doing so it has the remarkable "fore-sight" to prepare an escape hatch for the time when, as a moth, it will leave the gall. The moth, of course, will have no teeth or jaws fitted for cutting through the hard plant tissue and so would be unable to escape from the gall. For this reason the caterpillar cuts a circular opening in the wall near the top of the gall, and closes the entrance with silk. It then goes into its pupal stage during which it is transformed from a caterpillar into a moth. Eventually, in autumn, the moth emerges from its pupal case and pushes out through the thin, silken door and flies away

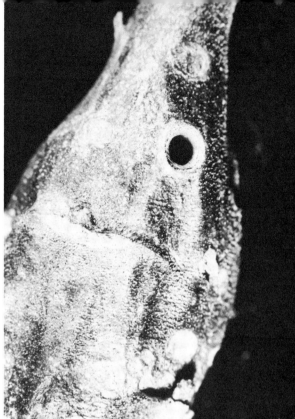

Left: The caterpillar then changes into the pupal stage and, when the moth eventually emerges, it pushes out through the silken door. Right: A goldenrod spindle gall out of which the adult moth has escaped. (Life size: 1/2 inch in diameter)

to mate. Thus, one full year is required for the completion of its life cycle.

While the goldenrod gall just discussed is created by a moth, other goldenrod galls result from the presence of attractive flies having "pictured" wings. These flies, about the size of houseflies, belong to the fruit fly family (Trypetidae) and the galls they produce on goldenrod stems are more common than those produced by the moths. These pretty flies spend the winter as larvae in the spherical stem galls of the goldenrod plants. As in the case of the caterpillar, the fly larva cuts an escape hatch in the wall of the gall but, instead of sealing the entrance with

31

Spherical goldenrod stem galls are common wherever goldenrods grow. These were created by flies (Eurosta).

silk, it merely leaves a thin skin of plant tissue as a door. This is done in the fall. With the arrival of spring, the larva changes into its pupal stage and, shortly thereafter, the adult fly emerges and pushes out through the thin-walled exit.

The fly's escape from its gall prison is interesting and worth observing. When ready to emerge from its pupal case in the gall, the fly inflates a balloon-like bladder from the front of its head. This is called the *ptilinum*. The inflation of this bladder pushes off the top of the pupal case and the fly then enters the tunnel it excavated as a larva in the thick wall of the gall. The outer end of this tunnel, you will recall, was left closed by a thin layer of tissue. When the fly reaches this thin door, it alternately inflates and deflates the bladder-like structure on its head and, eventually, breaks through the opening to the outside world. Once outside, the fly's ptilinum is withdrawn into its head and after half an hour or so its wings expand, enabling it to fly away.

Last fall, I collected a large number of goldenrod galls and cut them open with a sharp knife. I was astonished to find that many of them contained no fly larvae at all while others had

Within each spherical gall lives a plump grub, the larval stage of a fly. The thick walls of the gall furnish it with food and protection from most enemies.

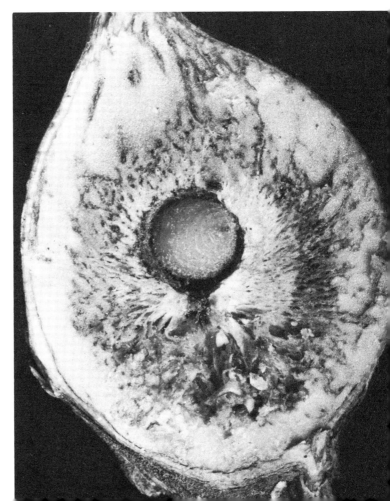

In spring, an attractive fly with black-mottled wings emerges from the gall and deposits its eggs in the stem of young goldenrods. (Life size: 1/4 inch across)

Even though the walls of the goldenrod galls are thick and tough, many insect enemies bore into them, often destroying the gall fly grubs. This gall contains a beetle grub that has destroyed the rightful owner.

been hollowed out and the fly larvae destroyed by other insects. Since the walls of these galls are quite thick and tough, one would assume that the hidden fly larvae would be safe from harm. However, such is not the case since many other insects bore into the galls to feed upon the helpless larvae or to devour the nutritious plant tissues. One of the most numerous of these destroyers is a small flower beetle (*Mordellistena unicolor*). In addition to this beetle, the hidden fly larvae have many other enemies. Woodpeckers hammer holes into the galls to capture them and squirrels and mice gnaw them open. Some of these enemies feed upon the larvae, others merely seek snug homes for the winter. While each goldenrod gall fly lays about fifty eggs, there are so many hazards that only a very small percentage of the young ever mature. In addition to various enemies, many of the larvae fail to provide escape doors to the outside and so the adult flies perish without ever seeing the light of day.

Other insects that take up residence in galls created by the true gall-forming kinds are called "guests" or *inquilines*. Many of these are closely related to the insects whose homes they invade but are, themselves, unable to cause gall formation. Many of these "guests" are, in a sense, "sheep in wolves' clothing." They feed for a time upon the tissues of the galls, then turn upon their hosts—the insects that created the galls—and devour them. Sometimes, several of these "guests" may be present in a gall at the same time.

By far the largest number of galls, as well as the most conspicuous, are those produced by gall wasps of the family Cynipidae. These wasps are very tiny in size and of characteristic form. If a number of cynipid galls are collected and placed in closed containers, the little wasps will emerge from their cells within the galls and can be studied under a microscope or a high-power hand lens.

Hedgehog galls are common on white oak leaves. They are covered with short spines created by gall wasps (Acraspis erinacei). (Life size: 1/4 inch in diameter)

The life histories of most of these cynipid wasps are very unusual; instead of their eggs developing into individuals like the parent insects, they grow into wasps that are entirely different in appearance and in habits. In fact, even the galls they produce are different from those from which they emerged. This is known as *alternation of generations* and occurs also in certain other insects. Thus, the wasps that emerge from one type of gall do not resemble their parents but do resemble their grandparents. As a matter of fact, there is so much difference between the wasps of succeeding generations that entomologists once thought that they were entirely different insects and so gave them different scientific names. It was not until 1873 that the truth concerning the relationship between one generation and the next was even suspected.

Probably the best way to understand how one generation of gall wasps follows the other is to take a common example such

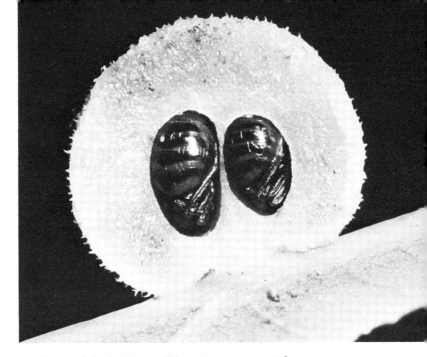

Within each hedgehog gall live from one to eight young wasps. In this cutaway view the larval wasps have already transformed into the pupal stage.

as the oak hedgehog gall created by a gall wasp (*Acraspis erinacei*). These galls are found on white oak leaves and are round or oblong with their surfaces covered with small spines. They occur on both surfaces of the leaves. When first formed these interesting galls are green, but by autumn they turn brown. Contained within each gall are from two to eight larval wasps, all of which will develop into females with very short wings. These females, without mating, then lay their eggs in the buds of the oak, usually in November. These eggs hatch the following May when small galls are produced on the bud scales. The wasps which emerge from these bud galls look entirely different from their female parents. Instead of being all females, they are of both sexes and have larger wings. They mate and the females then deposit their eggs in the young leaves of the oaks. It is from these eggs that emerge the larval wasps that stimulate the leaves to produce the typical hedgehog galls.

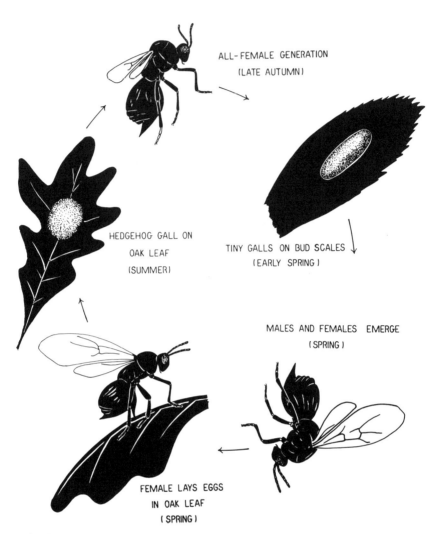

ALL-FEMALE GENERATION
(LATE AUTUMN)

HEDGEHOG GALL ON
OAK LEAF
(SUMMER)

TINY GALLS ON BUD SCALES
(EARLY SPRING)

MALES AND FEMALES EMERGE
(SPRING)

FEMALE LAYS EGGS
IN OAK LEAF
(SPRING)

Hedgehog gall wasps have very complicated life histories, as shown in these drawings. One wasp generation creates the typical hedgehog gall and the next, or alternate generation, produces tiny galls on the bud scales of the oaks. (Not drawn to scale)

Another common cynipid gall is the so-called "wool sower" gall produced by the activities of another cynipid wasp. These attractive galls are created on the oak twigs by mated females. They appear in spring. The galls are an inch or so in diameter and covered with white or pinkish "wool." From these galls emerge the next generation of wasps consisting only of females. These females lay their eggs beside the acorns where small, seed-like galls arise. From these galls emerge both males and females and the females, after mating, lay their eggs in twigs, causing the formation of the typical woolly galls.

It is obvious that the life histories of these little gall wasps are quite complex and, perhaps, a little hard to understand. As a general rule, the generation composed only of females appears in early spring and the tiny galls they produce grow very rapidly; by contrast, the next generation is made up of both sexes and arises in late spring or summer. The galls they produce are larger and develop very slowly. This is as one would expect, since galls produced in spring during the time of rapid plant growth naturally develop much faster than those arising later after the active growth of the trees or plants has slowed down. Some authorities believe that the all-female generation of gall wasps, since it emerges in spring during cool or cold weather, was evolved because of the difficulty of the females in finding mates at that time. Now that these individuals are all females and can lay fertile eggs without mating, there is no problem in this respect.

Just how many gall wasps have this type of life history is unknown. It seems probable that a large percentage of them do.

Almost everyone who spends much time in oak forests is familiar with the large, thin-walled galls known as oak-apples, some of which are as large as two inches in diameter and attached either to leaves or twigs. If one of these "apples" is cut open it will be found that the interior of the gall is filled with numerous fibers all radiating outward to its walls from a central core. If this core is cut open there will usually be found a plump little grub resting comfortably in a cell. This, of course, is the

One of the most attractive of all oak galls is the wool sower produced by a gall wasp (Callirhytes seminator). *It is covered with white or pink "wool." (Life size: 1 inch in diameter)*

larval wasp and it will eventually transform into the adult or winged stage. Soon, eggs are laid in oak leaves or twigs and the life cycle starts over again.

Witch-hazel cone galls are the end result of the activities of certain aphids or plant lice whose life history is even more complicated than that of the hedgehog gall wasp. In this case, also,

40

there is an alternation of generations. These aphids lay their eggs upon the branches and twigs of witch-hazel trees in late fall, each female depositing about ten eggs. In spring, the eggs hatch and produce females known as "stem mothers." These migrate to the leaves and begin feeding. Some substance secreted by the aphids causes the formation of the typical, conical galls. While the galls arise from the upper surfaces of the leaves, they are hollow and have openings extending out through the leaves' lower surfaces. Within these hollow galls, the "stem mothers," or unmated female aphids, produce numerous young. Eventually, the galls become filled with aphids and these, in time, emerge through the openings in the under surfaces of the leaves and fly to birch trees where they pass through several generations as wingless individuals. The sixth generation, on the

In cells hidden within these woolly galls live the larval wasps. When these mature and emerge, they create galls of another type on the acorns. In this photograph, taken in late autumn, the wasps have already emerged and the "wool" is dry and matted.

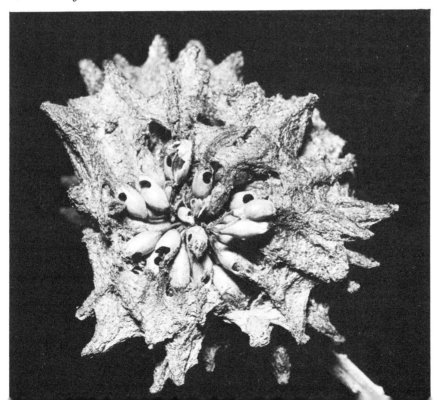

Of all common galls, the oak-apples are probably the most conspicuous and attractive. They are created by gall wasps (Cynips). *(Life size: 1½ inches in diameter)*

The walls of an oak-apple are very thin and the interior is filled with numerous fibers extending outward from a central core where the larval wasp lives and feeds.

The wasp larva that dwells in the oak-apple resembles a small grub. When full grown, it transforms into the pupal stage shown here. *(Life size: 1/8 inch)*

Eventually, the adult wasp emerges from its cell and gnaws its way out of the gall. Oak trees are favored by a large variety of gall-producing insects.

Here, an adult oak-apple wasp crawls away from its cell. To obtain this photograph, the cell had previously been removed from the gall. (Life size of wasp: 1/8 inch long)

This extreme close-up of an oak-apple wasp shows its details. After mating, this tiny wasp will deposit her eggs in young oak leaves, creating other oak-apple galls.

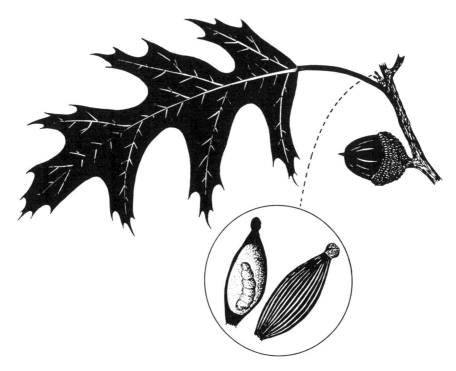

Tiny, ribbed galls found on certain oaks fall to the ground when mature and hop about like jumping beans. These unusual little galls are the products of cynipid wasps (Trisoleniella saltatus).

other hand, is winged and these aphids leave the birch trees and return to witch-hazel trees. These females then give birth to the seventh generation consisting of wingless males and females. These mate and eggs are laid. The aphids hatched from these eggs are the "stem mothers" that create the conical galls on the witch-hazel leaves. The life cycles of these aphids is, indeed, very strange and one wonders how it all began in the first place.

Probably the most remarkable of all galls are the jumping galls found on oaks in several parts of the United States. In a way, these galls remind one of Mexican jumping beans since

44

they hop about on the ground in the same way. In the case of Mexican jumping beans, the ability to hop about results from small caterpillars that live within the seed pods or "beans." When warmed by the hot sun the little caterpillar anchors its feet in the silken lining of the pod and flips its body, causing the "bean" to jump for an inch or more. The movements of jumping galls are caused in a similar way.

One type of jumping oak galls are created on the leaves of western valley oaks by small gall wasps (*Neuroterus saltitarius*). The galls are very tiny, about the size of radish seeds, and ellipsoidal in shape. They often occur in large numbers and, when mature, fall to the ground where the larval wasps flip their bodies about now and then, causing the galls to hop, often for some distance. It has been suggested that this aids the galls

In late summer or autumn, tiny galls of various shapes appear on the lower surfaces of hickory leaves, produced by hickory midge flies (Caryomyia).

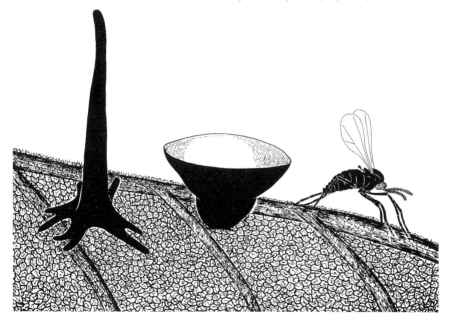

in finding lodging places in protective cracks or crevices where they will be safe from birds or other enemies. These "flea seeds," as they are often called, are frequently so abundant as to cover the ground where thousands of them may be seen hopping about at once.

Another jumping gall is the ribbed jumping gall originating on blue-jack or upland willow oaks that range from Florida to Texas and Oklahoma. They are also found on scarlet oaks growing in many areas of eastern United States. These galls are oblong in shape and have ribs extending lengthwise over their surfaces. They develop on the buds and are created by gall wasps. There are several other kinds of jumping galls but they are less common.

If you examine a number of hickory leaves in late summer and look closely you are apt to find some very tiny galls attached to their under surfaces. These galls vary greatly in form. Under a hand lens, some of them look like tiny fence posts while others remind one of goblets. Most of them are less than a quarter of an inch tall.

These strange small galls are the products of hickory midges, fragile flies with elongate, bead-like antennae, which belong to the gall gnat family (Cecidomyiidae). These hickory midges winter in the hickory galls and, in late May deposit their eggs on the undersides of the leaves. The female midge seems in no hurry; she crawls about over the hairy surface of the leaf, now and then pressing her ovipositor, or egg-tube, against the surface. After a moment or so a minute egg is ejected and she then searches about for another likely place. Within a few days a discolored spot appears on the leaf and, eventually, a gall develops. There are many different kinds of hickory midges, each one producing a characteristic gall. While most of the galls found on trees are produced in spring during the period of most

During rains, the cedar gall absorbs moisture, causing the spines to expand into gelatinous, spore-bearing "fingers."

The spores, carried by winds to apple trees, cause rust-colored spots on the leaves known as cedar-apple rust.

Some kinds of gall wasps seem incapable of producing their own galls. Instead, they lay their eggs in galls created by other gall makers. In this unusual photograph, such a gall wasp is seen in the act of inserting her egg into another wasp's gall.

active growth, these galls, by contrast, appear much later. I have often collected them as late as November.

We have already learned that conical witch-hazel galls are created by aphids. Aphids of another type, the phylloxeras, produce galls on a rather wide variety of trees and plants, including oaks, hickories, and chestnuts. Pecans, belonging to the hickory tribe, are also infested and frequently suffer considerable damage.

Phylloxera aphids have very complicated life histories, some more complex than others. A typical example is as follows: A female aphid, the "stem mother," hatches from an egg in the spring. She begins feeding, usually on a leaf, and a hollow gall

48

develops. Within this gall, the "stem mother," without mating, lays a number of eggs. These eggs, in turn, hatch into young aphids that grow into winged females. Again, without mating, these females lay eggs of two sizes; from the larger eggs, females emerge and from the smaller eggs, males. Mating now occurs and each female then lays a single egg, but this egg does not usually hatch until the following spring. It is from these eggs that the "stem mothers" emerge to begin the creation of the galls filled with colonies of phylloxera aphids.

So far we have considered only insect-produced galls, but other organisms, too, stimulate plants to create these unusual growths. One of these is a parasitic fungus, one that causes the growth of galls about the size of golf balls on cedar trees. When rains fall, long, gelatinous "fingers" push out of the surfaces of these galls and from them are shed millions of microscopic spores. Winds carry these spores to apple trees where they germinate, forming orange-yellow spots known as apple rust. The disease also affects the fruit. Later, fungus spores of another type are liberated from the apple leaves and blown back to the cedar trees where another crop of cedar galls is produced. Because the fungus alternates back and forth between apple and cedar trees, the disease is known as cedar-apple rust.

Spiny rose galls, caused by gall wasps (Diplolepis bicolor), *are also found on wild blackberry bushes.*

This unusual gall is quite common on cottonwood leaf stems. It is hollow and filled with aphids (Pemphigus populitransversus). *When the winged aphids are ready to leave the gall, a slit opens in the side, allowing them to escape.*

4

SOME GALLS OF FIELD
AND FOREST

Galls are created on plants of almost every family, from ferns to giant oaks. Probably the best places to study and collect them are in forested areas, especially those consisting of low, spreading trees whose branches and foliage can be reached from the ground. Cut-over areas are usually productive because in such places there are apt to be numerous small trees with succulent growth. Mountainous places are ideal if they are forested. I have found many galls on the oaks and other trees in southwestern United States. The Great Smoky Mountains are also productive. But plant galls are where you find them; they occur everywhere.

Not only do galls appear on trees but on many other plants as well. The goldenrods found growing along country roads harbor several kinds. In almost every patch of goldenrods there will be some whose stalks bear globular swellings about an inch in diameter. Often, several of these swellings will occur on the

The goldenrod spindle gall, left, was produced by a moth caterpillar (Gnorimoschema gallaesolidaginis), *while the spherical gall, right, resulted from the living activities of a fly larva* (Eurosta solidaginis).

same stem. Probably the best time to search for these galls is in winter or late fall after most of the foliage is gone. At this time, they are more easily seen.

If one of these spherical goldenrod galls is carefully cut open, a plump, white grub will be seen in a cell at the center. Do not be disappointed, however, if many of the galls contain only fragments of dry plant tissue or the small grubs of burrowing beetles. Many of the gall fly larvae fail to mature, victims of parasites or accidents. If a number of the stalks containing the galls are collected and placed in screened cages, the pretty flies will eventually emerge.

Perhaps a little less common than the spherical galls are the goldenrod spindle galls, created by a moth caterpillar. If these galls are cut open in summer, small caterpillars will usually be found inside. In any patch of goldenrods, a few will be found whose stalks are topped by masses of clustered leaves. These do not look like galls but they are, in truth, a type of gall, produced by midge flies (*Rhopalomyia*) that live in the growing buds.

There are also leaf galls of several kinds found on goldenrods. One of these is Clark's goldenrod gall, produced by a midge fly (*Rhopalomyia clarkei*). These are tiny, spindle-shaped galls marked with red. Gall flies of another kind (*R. anthophila*) create small, hairy galls of cylindrical form attached to the gold-colored flowers. These are called downy flower galls.

Sometimes, along roadsides or in fields, will be found yellow or golden, thread-like growths of love-vine or dodder (*Cuscuta*). This strange plant is a close relative of the morning-glory, one that has taken up a parasitic habit. Instead of manufacturing its own food as do most other plants, dodder attaches itself

Dodder is a parasitic vine that attacks clover and other plants. Upon its thread-like stems small gourd-shaped galls are often created by beetle larvae (Smicronyx sculpticollis) *that live inside.*

This strange gall found on a blackberry bush was produced by a gall wasp (Diastrophus nebulosus). *Many of the adult wasps have already emerged through exit holes.*

to clover or other plants and saps out the nutrients it needs to live. Dodder is, thus, an unusual plant with unusual habits. Just as unusual are the small, ovate galls produced on its thread-like stems. The galls themselves are not much different from those found on many other plants but what is unique is the fact that they are created by small beetle larvae. Very few beetles have taken up the gall-forming habit.

Often, along fences and in waste places, growths of wild blackberries are found. Several interesting galls develop on these plants. One is the attractive spiny rose gall, so-called because it also occurs on roses. These galls, produced by gall wasps, are covered with long, slender spines and their coloration varies from green to pastel shades of red or pink. Another blackberry gall, one that is less attractive, is the knot gall, also the product of a gall wasp. These are irregular swellings found on the stem. If observed in late summer or autumn, many exit holes will be noticed. It is out of these openings that the mature wasps have emerged.

Another rose gall, one I have also found on blackberry, is the attractive regal rose gall, created by a gall wasp (*Diplolepis gracilis*). These little galls are only about one-eighth inch in diameter, but their shape is quite unusual; they look like tiny crowns with projections around their margins. It is because of this shape that they are called "regal" galls.

Those who live in the West will find several galls on sage brush. One of these, the most common, is the sage brush bladder gall, produced by a midge fly. These are soft, fleshy swellings attached to the leaves.

Almost any weed patch or waste area containing lush growths

These soft, fleshy galls on western sage brush are the work of midge flies (Diarthronomyia occidentalis).

Galls of unusual form are found on hackberry trees. These top-shaped ones attached to a hackberry leaf were created by gall midge flies (Phytophaga).

of wild plants will yield galls of one kind or another. There are hundreds of kinds and a little diligence will reveal them.

Probably the most abundant and perhaps the most interesting galls are those found on trees. Some kinds of trees have more galls than others, but they almost all have galls, produced by gall-making insects, mites, fungi, or microscopic organisms. Because of their abundance and variety, oak and hickory galls are covered in a separate chapter.

Hackberry trees (*Celtis*) are found in many parts of the United States, from Wyoming and the Dakotas eastward. These trees have many galls, especially on the leaves, most of which are caused by midge flies. One is a top-shaped gall created by a midge (*Phytophaga*). Of all the hackberry galls, these have the most interesting shapes. Unusual because they are the product of jumping plant lice (family Psyllidae) are the hackberry button galls of which there are several kinds. As their name implies, they resemble tiny buttons.

Hackberry twig galls are not as common as the leaf galls, but there is one kind that is frequently seen. These have no common name but are globular in form and created by larval midges (*Cecidomyia*).

Close-up of top-shaped hackberry gall. (Life size: 1/4 inch)

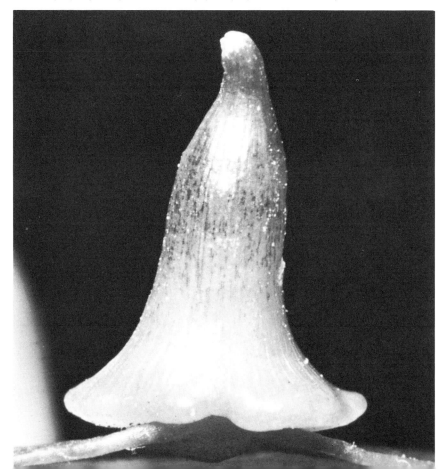

Hackberry gall produced by a gall midge fly.

Previous gall cut open to show midge fly larva. (Life size: 1/8 inch in diameter)

A hackberry button gall. (Life size: 1/8 inch in diameter)

Another kind of hackberry button gall. (Life size: 1/8 inch in diameter)

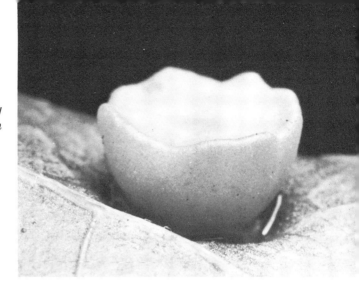

Hackberry twig galls, produced by midge flies. (Life size: 3/8 inch in diameter)

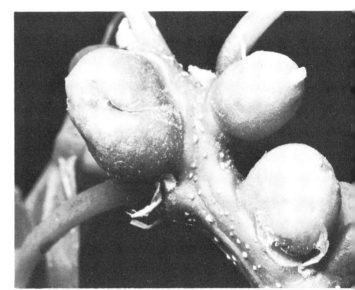

Spiny gall of hackberry, created by jumping plant lice (family Psyllidae). (Life size: 3/8 inch in diameter)

Linden or basswood (*Tilia*) trees are fairly common in eastern United States where their wood finds considerable use in industry. The flowers yield large quantities of honey, noted for its excellent flavor. Galls of several kinds are found on both the twigs and the leaves. Probably the most common of the leaf galls are tiny, finger-like growths produced by mites. They arise from the upper surfaces of the leaves and are often quite abundant on every leaf.

Elms are popular shade trees in many localities but few gall makers attack them. However, one often finds the leaves covered with small finger-like galls, the homes of aphids.

Witch-hazel trees (*Hamamelis*) grow wild only in eastern United States and eastern Asia. Their peculiar little flowers open in midwinter and the hard seeds, which mature in autumn, are snapped out of their pods with great force. Almost everywhere these trees are found they furnish dwelling places for two kinds of gall-making aphids. One of these is the witch-hazel cone gall found on the upper surfaces of the leaves. The complicated life history of this aphid (*Hormaphis hamamelides*) was discussed in a previous chapter. Cone galls appear in summer. Another aphid-produced gall of this tree is the spiny witch-hazel gall, created on the twig buds by another aphid (*Hamamelistes spinosus*). Like the aphid that produces the cone gall, the spiny gall aphid spends one part of its life cycle on birch trees.

Willows are common almost everywhere, as are several very characteristic galls found on them. One of these is the pine-cone gall, so-called because of its resemblance to a small pine cone. These are usually attached to the tips of the twigs and are produced by a gall midge (*Rhabdophaga strobiloides*). Other willow galls are the products of sawflies, or leaf-eating wasps. Only a few sawflies, however, have taken up the gall-forming habit.

These tiny finger-like galls on linden leaves were produced by mites (Erio-phyes). (Life size: 1/4 inch tall)

Close-up of mite galls on linden leaf. (Life size: 1/4 inch tall)

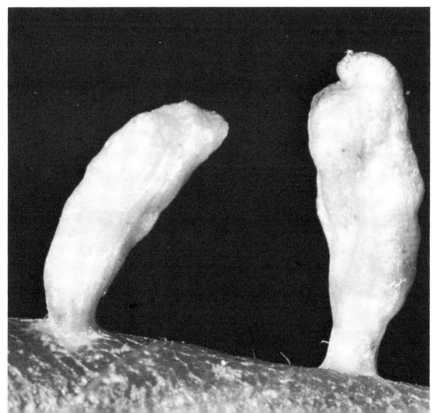

Closely related to the willows are the poplars and they, too, are hosts to several gall makers. These include midge flies, beetles, mites, and aphids. Probably the most unusual are the leaf-stem galls produced by aphids. These galls consist of swellings on the leaf stems or petioles, and if they are cut open it will be found that their inner cavities are filled with aphids. When the aphids have reached the stage in their development when they are ready to leave the galls, transverse slits appear in the sides of the galls. These exits slowly open and out come the winged aphids. Eggs are laid and the cycle starts over again the next season.

Like most other forest trees, maples have galls of several kinds. Many of these are created by mites, while others result from insects. One of the most common is the maple leaf spot which is not really a gall in the usual sense. Rather, they are yellow, red-margined eye-spots on the leaves and are very conspicuous. Often there are many of these on a single leaf, mak-

Often, finger-like growths are found on elm leaves. They are galls created by aphids. (Life size: 3/8 inch tall)

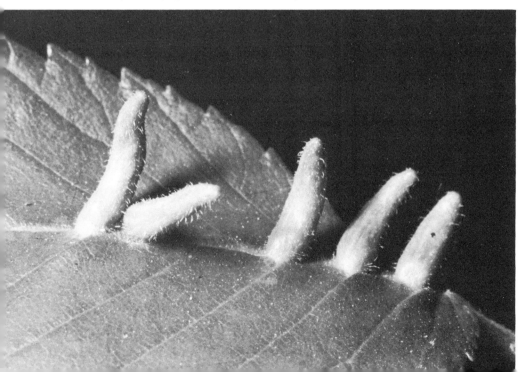

Witch-hazel trees are usually hosts to galls of two kinds, both produced by aphids. One is the cone gall, while the other, shown here, is the spiny witch-hazel gall. (Life size: 1/2 inch)

ing it stand out among the rest of the foliage. These eye-spots are the homes of larval midge flies.

Those who live in regions where dogwood trees abound are fortunate in several respects; the snowy blooms appear in early spring to enliven the forests and their leaves turn scarlet in autumn. There are also several galls found on these attractive trees, the most common of which consists of swellings of the smaller twigs. Within each of these enlargements dwells the creator of the gall, a reddish, midge fly larva. These larvae become full grown in September and drop to the ground where they pass the winter. The adult flies emerge the next spring and lay their eggs in the dogwood shoots.

One of the most abundant and characteristic of all the trees of the swamps and bayous of southeastern United States is the bald cypress, so called because it sheds its foliage in late au-

63

Very conspicuous on the leaves of maples are colorful eye-spot galls. These flattened galls are produced by gall midge flies (Cecidomyia occelaris).

Inside this swelling on a dog-wood twig lives a red, larval insect, the young stage of a gall midge (Mycodiplosis alternata).

Among the most unusual of all galls are these pretty flower-like ones found on bald cypress leaves. Within them live young gall midges (Itonida anthici).

tumn. Upon its needle-like leaves are often found some unusual galls that resemble small, white flowers. These are known as cypress flower galls and are now known to be created by gall wasps. At one time, however, it was believed that they were caused by a parasitic fungus.

Pines, also, have a number of galls. One kind consists of swellings at the base of the needles. These galls are the work of midge flies.

Bullet galls, common on oak twigs, are usually very hard. They are produced by gall wasps (Disholcaspis). (Life size: 1/2 inch in diameter)

These tiny galls were produced by hickory midge flies (Caryomyia).

5

GALLS OF OAKS AND HICKORIES

Of all trees, the oaks are most favored by gall-making insects. Galls of one sort or another may be found on almost every kind of oak and on almost every part of the trees from the roots to the flowers, acorns, and leaves.

Root galls of the oaks are rarely seen by the amateur, but galls that occur on the twigs and other parts of trees are plentiful and easy to find. Almost all twig galls are caused by gall wasps (family Cynipidae) and they are of almost infinite form and coloration. Perhaps the most common kinds are the bullet galls, marble-like growths occurring either singly or in clusters of two or three. They result from the activities of certain gall wasps. Usually these galls are about half an inch in diameter and very hard. They are most easily seen in winter after the leaves are gone. Another twig gall is the fig gall found on oaks of several kinds. They, also, are produced by gall wasps. Still another twig gall, one also found on the branches, is the horned oak gall created by another gall wasp on scrub, pin, and other oaks.

Oak fig galls are created on the twigs by gall wasps (Disholcaspis spongiosa). *(Life size: 1½ inches in diameter)*

These galls, often as large as two inches in diameter, have horn-like projections. They are quite common. Yet another twig gall frequently seen in winter is the gouty oak gall, also created by a wasp. These are globular, often of irregular form, and vary from one to three inches in diameter. They occur on several kinds of oaks. Both fig and gouty gall wasps have complex life histories; they alternate between small blister galls on the leaves and the typical twig galls. Several years are required for the completion of their life cycles.

Unique among oak twig galls are the pretty wool sower galls found on white oaks. These appear in May or June and look like globular masses of white or pink cotton surrounding the twigs. If one of these peculiar galls is cut open, the cells containing the gall wasp larvae may be seen.

Easily identified by its spines or horns is the horned oak gall, produced by gall wasps (Plagiotrochus cornigerus). (Life size: 2 inches in diameter)

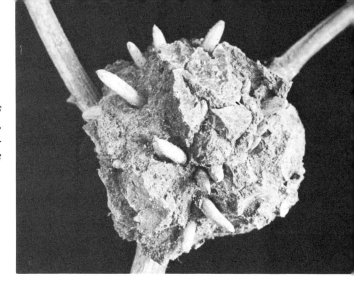

The gouty oak gall is the home of gall wasp larvae (Plagiotrochus punctatus). (Life size: 2 inches in diameter)

Shown here is a gouty oak gall from which the adult wasps have already emerged.

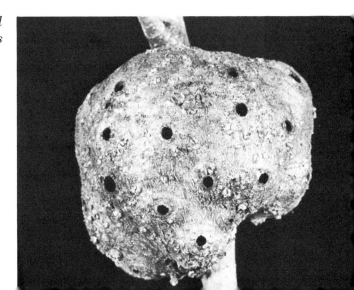

This peculiar gall was created on a willow oak twig by a gall wasp (Callirhytes difficilis). *(Life size: 1/8 inch tall)*

Less common than the galls discussed above is the fluted oak gall found on water oak. These little structures are about a quarter of an inch tall and shaped something like little tops with fluted sides. Within them dwell tiny wasp larvae (*Disholcaspis*).

Rarely, on willow, water, and some other oaks, appear strange little galls created by wasps of another kind. I have found but one specimen, the one from which the above photograph was made. Like many uncommon galls, it has no common name.

There are hundreds of oak leaf galls, many of which are peculiar or pretty and they range in size from very minute to an inch or more in diameter. Most of them appear on the leaves in spring, the time of rapid growth. Thus, they should be looked for in that season. They may be attached to either the leaf blades or to the leaf stems or *petioles*. A number of leaf galls do not appear until late summer or even in autumn, but these develop more slowly and are harder than the spring galls. Most autumn galls eventually fall to the ground and the wasps do not emerge until the next year. In some kinds, the galls may lie on the ground for as long as five years before the winged adult wasps emerge.

Among the more attractive and conspicuous of the leaf galls are the large oak-apple galls. These look like small apples, as their name implies, and they range in diameter from one to two inches. They are either bright green or mottled. If one of them is cut open, it will be found to be hollow with numerous fibers radiating outward from a central core. It is in this core that the wasp larva dwells. Similar galls are often found attached to the twigs. These latter are the creations of another wasp (*Amphibolips*). Most oak-apple galls hang suspended from the leaves or their stems but there is one kind that grows half above the leaf surface and half below. Like other apple galls, it is produced by a cynipid wasp.

While oak-apple galls of most kinds hang from the twigs or leaves, this one arises partly above and partly below the leaf surface. (Life size of gall: 1½ inches in diameter)

An uncommon little oak twig gall is the fluted gall,
produced on water oak twigs by a gall wasp (Disholcaspis). *(Life size: 1/4 inch tall)*

Oak vase galls are of unusual shape. These, created by gall wasps (Andricus), were found on a shin oak leaf in Colorado. *(Life size: 1/4 inch tall)*

Knobby oak galls arise in clusters at the bases of the leaves. Young gall wasps (Andricus rugatus) *live in them. (Life size: 1/4 inch)*

One of the most attractive galls encountered in my studies was the spiny-vase gall, the product of a gall wasp (*Xanthoteras*). These unusual little galls were found in clusters on post oak leaves were very pretty when viewed under a hand lens. They were found in late autumn.

As with the famed Princes of Serendip, who were always finding interesting things while looking for something else, my most unusual finds have occurred while I was searching for some other plant or animal wonder. I was once in Colorado studying honey ants when I accidentally noticed a cluster of tiny vase-shaped galls on the leaf of a shin oak. These little galls, hardly an eighth of an inch tall, resembled little vases and were, I

73

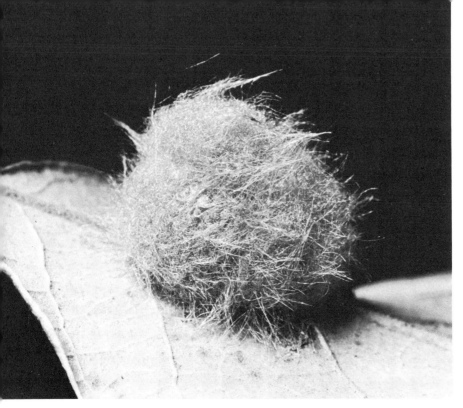

This hairy gall on an oak leaf was created by a gall wasp
(Acraspis villosa). *(Life size: 1/2 inch)*

found, the creations of gall wasps. Again, while photographing wild flowers in the Great Smoky Mountains, I accidentally discovered some knobby galls on white oaks, a product of another kind of wasp. In another case, while attempting to identify a small bird in another oak in that same area, I noticed some hairy growths on the leaves. These turned out to hairy oak galls, also produced by gall wasps. On this same tree, I was fortunate enough to find a cluster of little spiny galls, the creations of cynipid wasps.

Chance certainly plays an important role in a naturalist's findings. While searching for firewood along Little River in the Smoky Mountains, I casually glanced at the leaves of a small oak and was pleased to see a gall I had not previously photographed. This was a woolly fold gall that, when cut open, proved

These hairy galls of another kind contained the larvae of gall wasps. (Life size: 1/4 inch)

to be filled with tiny fly larvae, later determined as being young gall midges.

Gall midge flies produce a number of other galls on oaks, some of unusual form. Among these are the oak spangles, rather common little button-like galls on white oak leaves. A leaf covered with these galls looks as if it were covered with tiny sequins.

Anyone who studies galls in oak forests is certain, eventually, to find roly-poly galls. These are spherical in shape and often as large as an inch in diameter. One of the more common of these is the succulent roly-poly gall, produced by a gall wasp. I found these to be abundant on the leaves of the scarlet oaks. They were mottled green and attached to leaves that had been deformed as the galls had increased in size. When one of the

Clusters of button galls are often seen on white oak leaves. They look like little sequins and are the work of gall midge flies (Cecidomyia). *(Life size: 1/8 inch)*

galls was cut open, a hollow cavity was exposed and in this cavity rested a small white sphere. The sphere was loose and rolled about inside the gall. If an unopened gall was shaken, this sphere rattled about like a pea in a dry pod.

Within the little spheres that roll about inside the roly-poly galls live the larval wasps that create them. Since they are not attached to the walls of the galls, there is some question as to how they obtain their nourishment. It has been speculated that perhaps it is absorbed through the wall of the capsule. Like many other cynipid gall wasps, those that create roly-poly galls have an alternation of generations; one generation of wasps produces the typical roly-poly galls and the next generation produces tiny, white galls attached to the surfaces of the oak leaves.

Woolly fold galls apparently develop as enlargements of the leaf veins of oak leaves. Within the hollow galls live young gall midges (Cecidomyia). *(Life size: 1 inch long)*

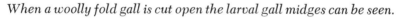

When a woolly fold gall is cut open the larval gall midges can be seen.

Roly-poly galls are formed on various kinds of oak leaves by gall wasp larvae (Andricus palustris). They are soft and fleshy. (Life size: 1/2 inch)

When cut open, a roly-poly gall is found to contain a white, pearl-like sphere. It is within it that the wasp larva lives.

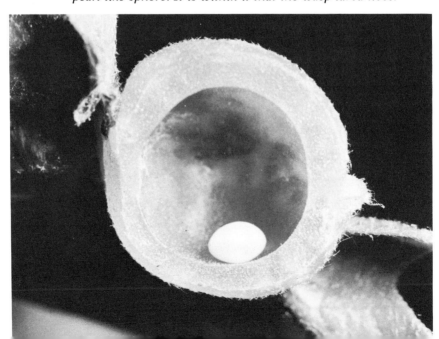

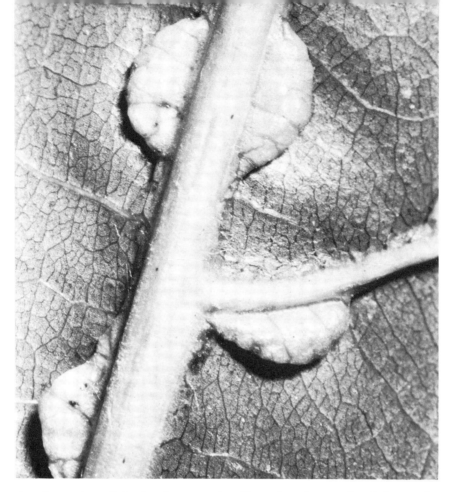

Another vein gall is the shrimp-tail gall produced on red oak leaves by gall midges (Cecidomyia). *(Life size: 1/4 inch long)*

Many galls seem to arise almost anywhere on a leaf while others are confined to the veins or the mid-ribs. Often, in autumn, small clusters of attractive galls are found attached to the mid-ribs of white oak leaves. Under a lens, these little galls remind one of diminutive peaches of rosy-pink hue. Strangely, these pretty little galls have no common name but they are the homes of gall wasps. Another vein gall is one I call, for lack of a better name, the shrimp-tail gall. They do, indeed, resemble tiny shrimp tails and always occur along the larger leaf veins of red oaks. They are produced by gall midges.

79

These little galls, attached to the leaf of a white oak, are marked with pink and resemble tiny peaches. In them live gall wasp larvae (Cynips dimorphus). (Life size: 1/8 inch)

When seen close-up these little "peach" galls are found to be covered with fine hair.

This leafy bud gall of live oak does not look like a gall, but within it live larval gall wasps (Andricus foliatus). *(Life size: 3/8 inch)*

On a deserted country road I recently found clusters of very pretty galls attached to the leaves of scarlet oaks. These galls, about one-eighth inch tall, were bright red in color and reminded me of little red jugs with white stoppers. They were, I found, the product of cynipid gall wasps.

Some galls do not look like galls at all, and the beginner may easily be deceived into believing them to be products of normal growth. Leafy bud galls, for instance, resemble clusters of bud scales. Such galls occur on many oaks, a good example being the leafy bud gall of live oak. It is the creation of a gall wasp.

Second in importance to the oaks as havens for gall makers are trees of the walnut family. To this family belong the hickories, walnuts, pecans, and some other trees. While the oaks are favored by the gall wasps (family Cynipidae), the leaves of hickories are the chosen site for gall formation by aphids or plant lice and by the gall midge flies (family Cecidomyiidae).

81

Phylloxera galls, caused by aphids, are common on hickory leaves.

The hickory aphids, known as phylloxeras, are closely related to the destructive grape phylloxera and the galls they produce appear in spring. They are of many forms; some look like mere blisters on the leaves, while others are globular. If one of these phylloxera galls is cut open it will be found to be hollow and filled with aphids. Sometimes this cavity is so full of aphids that there is not even "standing room" for them. Usually, if these galls are opened in late spring, it will be found that openings have appeared, either through the lower leaf surfaces or through the tops of the galls. It is out of these openings that the winged aphids leave when the time is proper. It is remarkable, indeed, that the development of the galls is so timed that when the aphids are ready to leave, the exits are obligingly opened for them.

Other hickory phylloxera galls resemble small gourds. (Life size: 3/8 inch tall) (See next photograph)

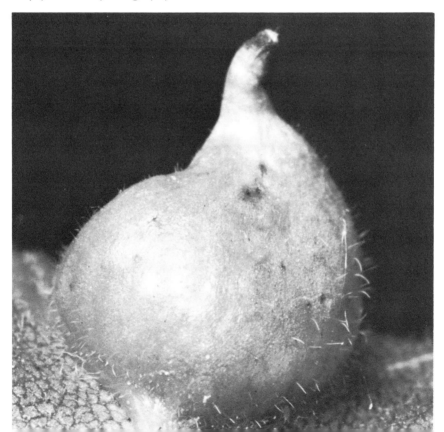

When the gall in the previous photograph was cut open, the phylloxera aphids inside were exposed. Eventually, the winged aphids will escape through the opening at the top.

Some phylloxera galls have their openings through the lower surface of the leaf, as this photograph shows. The aphids seen inside have not yet reached the winged stage and are not ready to leave the gall.

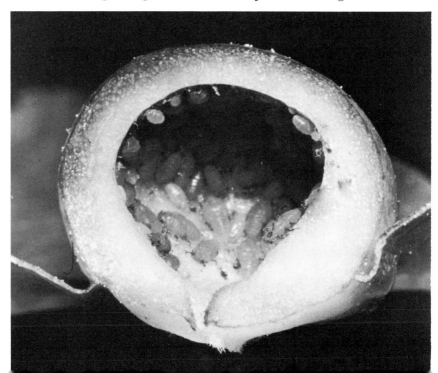

This odd-looking gall found on hickory leaves is the work of hickory midge flies. (See next photographs)

Many, perhaps most, of the galls found on hickory leaves are the work of hickory midges, small, mosquito-like flies (*Caryomyia*). The galls they produce are of many shapes; they vary from tiny spheres and slender tubes to others that look like little dunce caps. Look for these galls in late summer on the lower surfaces of the leaves.

The midges responsible for these unusual little galls spend winter in the galls and the winged flies appear in late May.

85

In late summer the strange little galls of hickory midge flies (Caryomyia) *are often found on the under surfaces of hickory leaves. Their shapes vary from dunce caps and tubes to posts and spheres.*

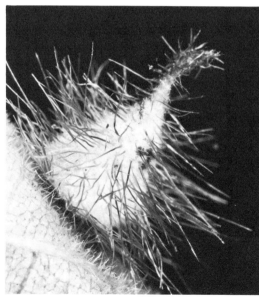

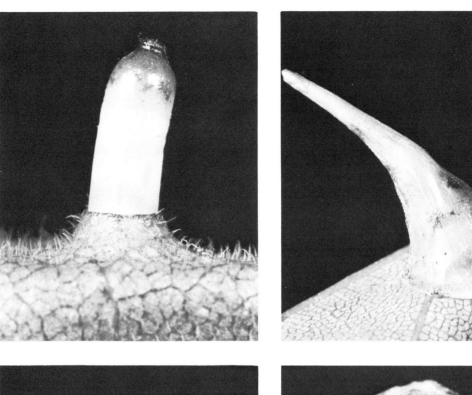

Frequently, pines are damaged by the presence of large numbers of galls, produced on their needles by gall midges (Contarinia).

6

HISTORY AND IMPORTANCE
OF GALLS

In the modern world plant galls are of interest chiefly because
of their remarkable forms and the manner by which they are
produced. However, even before the arrival of modern medicine and the development of the newer types of dyes, galls were
an important item of commerce. As late as 1945, 550,367 pounds
of galls were imported into the United States from Turkey.
These galls were used in medicine or the chemical substances
they contained were extracted for use in industry.

There is no way of knowing when galls were first used. There
is evidence that they were in use as medicaments at least five
hundred years B.C. Later, Pliny, the Roman naturalist (A.D. 23
to 79), recorded twenty-three remedies compounded from plant
galls. These included affections of the gums, burns, and other
human ailments. Pliny also stated that powdered galls, when
mixed with honey, were valuable in restoring hair, and that

Within this hard, thick-walled oak gall lives a larval wasp. From such galls, rich in tannic acid and other substances, excellent ink was once made.

powdered gall was effective in the treatment of venomous insect stings. That the uses of galls for such purposes were not without medicinal value is evidenced by the fact that, over two thousand years later, the *United States Pharmacopoeia* lists a preparation of galls, known as *Unguentum gallae,* as being efficacious as an astringent in the treatment of burns and hemorrhoids.

The galls most used in medicine were Aleppo galls, known also as Smyrna galls or oak-apples, which were gathered from shrub-like oaks (*Quercus infectoria*) found in Asia Minor. These galls, usually called gallnuts, were up to an inch in diameter and created by a tiny gall wasp (*Cynips gallae-tinctoriae*). Gallnuts were of several different grades, depending upon when they were gathered. If collected from the oaks before the wasps had emerged they were blue, green, or black and known as "black" galls. After the wasps had emerged the galls became lighter in hue and were then called "white" gallnuts. These latter brought a higher price on the market.

Gallnuts contain from 50 per cent to 75 per cent tannic acid, 2 per cent to 4 per cent gallic acid, as well as resin, calcium oxalate, and starch. Of all the oak galls found in the United States, a Texas oak gall contains the largest amount of tannic acid. This gall resembles the Aleppo gall and contains 40 per cent of this acid. It is produced on a Texas live oak by a gall wasp (*Disholcaspis cinerosa*) and is known as the mealy oak gall. It is spherical in shape and grows attached to the twigs. Another gall, the red pouch gall found on sumac (*Rhus*), is a most attractive gall, being suffused by pastel shades of rose-red. It is produced by aphids or plant lice (*Melaphis rhois*). These pouch-like galls are thin-walled and large numbers of the aphids can be seen if the gall is cut open. Such galls are rich in tannic acid; the dried galls contain about 60 per cent of this useful chemical. There is, however, a Chinese gall that contains nearly 70 per cent tannic acid, or tannin.

Tannic acid, so often found in plant galls, is a yellowish-white substance with a characteristic odor and a bitter, astringent taste. It is soluble in water and alcohol and, when mixed with iron salt such as ferric chloride, forms a blue precipitate. As a result of this latter quality, an excellent ink is produced when powdered gallnut is mixed with ferric chloride or copperas. In practice, a small amount of gum arabic is added to give body to the ink. Ink made in this manner was used for nearly a thousand years, probably having first been used by monks in the copying of manuscripts. Such ink is permanent and for this reason has been specified for official use by the United States Treasury, the Bank of England, the German Chancellery, and the Danish Government. Almost all the old court records were written with quill pens using gall ink.

In *Waltharilied*, a Latin epic of the tenth century written by a Swiss monk, Ekkehard I, it is stated that ". . . all ink comes from gall apples and all gall apples from a wicked wasp's sting." The remarkable thing is that, even then, it was known that oak galls resulted from the activities of certain wasps.

In the making of ink, the proportions were as follows:

Powdered oak gall	6 ounces	Gum arabic	4 ounces
Copperas	6 ounces	Water	6 pints

In former years gall inks were also used for the writing of secret messages. Here is how it was done: The secret message was written on paper with a quill pen dipped in a copperas solution. Usually, to avoid suspicion that a secret communication was present, the message was written between the lines of some unimportant but visible message. The recipient of the letter placed the paper in a shallow tray containing an infusion of oak gall. This allowed the tannin from the gall to react with the copperas, making the writing visible.

Until recently, Aleppo and certain other galls constituted an important source of dye for imparting dark colors to fur and

Gall ink was made by mixing copperas (ferrous sulphate) with crushed oak gall. Gum arabic was added to give the ink its adhesive quality.

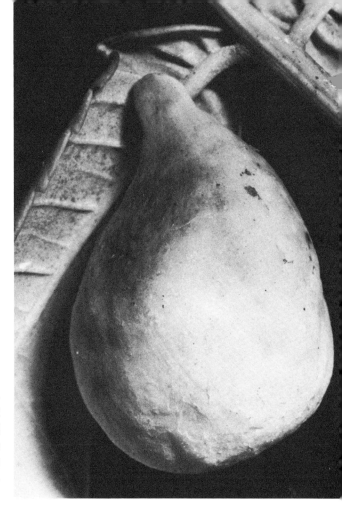

*Red pouch galls found on su-
mac are tinged with red and
are thin-walled. Contained
within their hollow cavities are
numerous aphids* (Melaphis
rhois). *(Life size: 1 inch in diameter)*

other garments, especially those made of wool. In the days when
St. Louis, Missouri, was an important fur center, large quantities
of gallnuts were imported and used in the dressing and dyeing
of skins. Since these galls contained large amounts of tannin,
they were valuable in the tanning of leather. Later, other
cheaper sources of tannin were found. In the ancient days, the
value of gall extracts in dyeing was recognized and they were
used to dye hair black. In East Africa, dye from gallnuts was
used by Somali women for the making of tattooing inks.

A gall known variously as the mad apple of Sodom, Dead Sea
fruit, Mecca gall, or Bussorah gall was once used in Palestine,

Albania, and Italy for the making of Turkey red dye. This gall is produced on oak trees by a gall wasp (*Cynips insana*). The dye was considered to be superior to that extracted from Aleppo galls.

In some places and times insect galls have been used as sources of food, probably because of their high content of starches and sugars. On the Isle of Crete large galls produced on sage (*Salvia pomifera*) by a gall wasp (*Aulax*) are sweet to the taste and are collected and sold in May. They have an acid, aromatic flavor and are mixed with honey. This gall is known locally as "*pomme de sauge.*"

In Mexico, large oak galls produced by a gall wasp (*Dishol-caspis weldi*) are very sweet to the taste and frequently sold in fruit stands. Here in the United States, the catmint gall, formed on catmint by a gall wasp (*Aylax glechomae*), has a very pleasant taste and odor like the plant upon which it grows. These small, spherical galls are often eaten.

In Missouri and Arkansas, a black cynipid gall has sometimes been so abundant on oaks as to constitute an important food source for cattle, hogs, sheep, turkeys, and chickens. Such galls are reported to be of special value in fattening hogs. They are of small size and known locally as "black oak wheat." The insect that produces them is a gall wasp, but authorities differ as to the name of the wasp that causes them. One authority lists it as *Callirhytes*, while another states that the galls are created by *Dryocosmus deciduus*. In any case, these abundant galls seem to have a very high food content as is evident from their analyses. They contain 12 per cent moisture, 8.56 per cent protein, 63.6 per cent starch and other carbohydrates, while the remainder consists of fiber and other substances.

Perhaps one of the most remarkable things about these strange plant growths is that the American Indian apparently

94

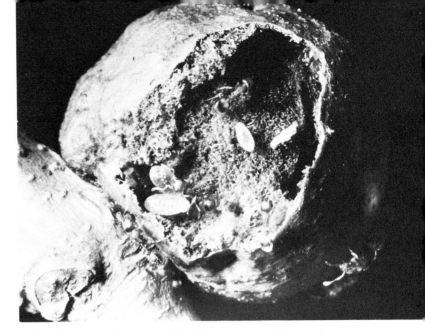

Old, abandoned insect galls often serve as homes for small colonies of ants. In this photograph, a cynipid gall has been cut open, exposing a colony of such ants and their white young.

made no use of them. Abundant as they are on oaks of the Southwest, it is indeed peculiar that the early Indians, as far as is known, did not discover this readily available source of astringents, tanning material, and food. These early Americans lived close to nature and made use of almost every plant and animal product found in the vicinities of the places where they lived. In spite of lack of information in this regard, it seems highly probable that they did make some sort of use of plant galls. It would be strange, indeed, if they had not done so.

There are a number of insect galls that, for some but little understood reason, secrete considerable quantities of honey-like honeydew upon their outer surfaces. Seemingly, this sweet substance results from an excess production of sugar by the gall as it develops.

Gall honeydew is often so abundant that it is gathered and stored by honeybees and honey ants. Galls produced on valley oaks (*Quercus lobata*) in California by a gall wasp (*Dishol-caspis eldoradensis*) secrete so much honeydew that local honeybees may gather and store from 30 to 40 pounds per hive in a season. This honeydew flow commences about the middle of August and continues until November. The quality of this gall honey is, however, rather poor as far as human consumption is concerned.

In southwestern United States and Mexico are found certain ground-dwelling ants known as honey ants (*Myrmecocystus*). Each night, during summer, the worker ants stream out of their underground nests and hurry across the stony soil to nearby shin oaks. Up the trunks and branches they crawl until they reach the numerous, spherical galls growing attached to the twigs. These galls are covered with sweet honeydew which the ants imbibe until their abdomens are nearly twice natural size. When the workers' abdomens will hold no more, they hurry back to their nests and feed the honeydew to certain individuals known as *repletes*. Just how these repletes are chosen to serve as honey tanks is unknown, but in any case these individuals hang suspended by their feet from the ceilings of the subterranean galleries while their abdomens gradually increase in size. The "field force" of workers continues to feed them load after load of honeydew. Eventually, each replete's abdomen swells to the size of a small grape and it is then almost helpless; it cannot crawl about and if it should fall to the floor of the gallery, it is usually unable to climb back to its position. Often, in such a fall, its thin-walled abdomen is ruptured and the sweet contents flow across the floor.

Honey ant repletes constitute the colony's only source of stored food. This is important since the galls from which the honeydew is harvested are productive only during the summer months. During autumn, winter, and spring, honeydew cannot

Galls of several kinds secrete sweet honeydew from their outer surfaces which honeybees and honey ants often gather and store. The honey ants feed it to certain individual ants that serve as living honey tanks for the colony's food supply. Here, such an ant, its abdomen swollen with honeydew, hangs suspended from the ceiling of the nest.

be gathered, so the ants, when hungry, approach the repletes who regurgitate droplets of honeydew for them. Thus, these ants have evolved a food-storage habit enabling them to survive in a region where their food can be harvested for only a short period each year. Probably the best place to observe the habits of these remarkable ants is in Colorado's Garden of the Gods. Ants with similar habits are found also in Australia and South Africa.

The relationships between insects and plant galls are often quite complex. The formation of galls is, of course, stimulated by insects or other forms of plant or animal life. In a number of cases, however, fungi of various kinds grow inside the galls and, possibly, are fed upon by the larvae that dwell there. The larvae of certain mosquito-like midge flies (family Itonididae) found living in plant galls are always associated with fungi. It seems probable that the fungus spores are introduced into the plant at the time that the female midge deposits her eggs. Whether her larvae are benefited by the presence of the fungus is unknown. Some authorities believe that the growing fungus helps the midge larvae indirectly by breaking down the gall tissues, making them more easily digestible.

So far we have considered plant galls as being merely of scientific interest or as sources of dyes, inks, or other substances. In truth, many kinds of gall-forming insects, mites, fungi, and viruses cause serious damage to the plants they infest or infect. Often, oak and other galls damage plants or trees to a serious extent. This is especially true in cases where large numbers are present. One of the most destructive, as well as the best known of these, is the grape phylloxera (*Phylloxera vitifoliae*). A pest of native grapes in the United States, this aphid was accidentally introduced into France about 1860. By 1875 it had destroyed nearly one-third of the vineyards consisting of 2,500,000 acres.

Galls of some kinds are important because of the damage they do to the plants and trees upon which they occur. This large oak tree, photographed in winter after it had shed its leaves, contains thousands of gouty oak galls.

These insects create galls on both leaves and roots, alternating from one to the other. The most severe damage is done to the roots. For a time it appeared that the grape wine industry of France was doomed; then it was discovered that control of the pests could be achieved by grafting European varieties on the rootstocks of American grapes which are resistant to attack. In this manner, the French grape industry was saved.

Pines are often infested with gall midges that create galls on the needles. In some cases, the trees are severely damaged.

The hessian fly, a serious pest of wheat, is a gall midge (*Phytophaga destructor*). It is a native of Europe, having been accidentally introduced into the United States.

In addition to insect gall producers, there are several fungi that cause gall-like growths on plants. One of these is white-pine blister rust which causes enlargements on the smaller limbs. In spring, yellow masses of dust-like spores are discharged from the outer surfaces of the galls and these spores are carried by winds to currant and gooseberry bushes where the next stage in the life cycle of the fungus is spent.

This wild grape leaf has many phylloxera galls, each containing a number of the insects. Grape phylloxeras once threatened the wine industry of France.

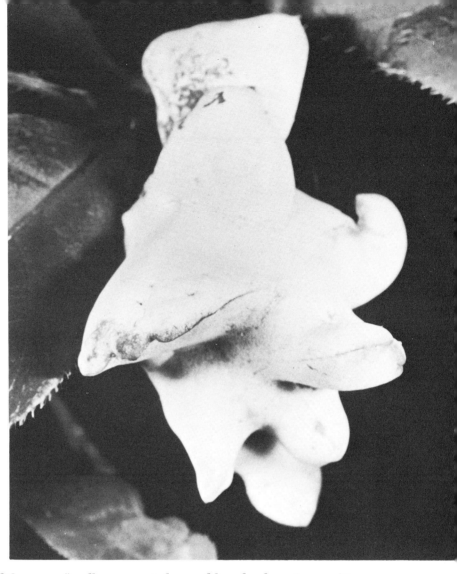

This "cauliflower ear" gall was created on wild azalea by a fungus (Exobasidium vaccinii). These galls are sometimes known as "pinkster apples."

Greenhouse, garden, and wild azaleas are frequently infected by a fungus that causes peculiar enlargements or swellings of the petals and leaves. These are called "pinkster apples." Sometimes they are eaten.

Crown gall, caused by a bacterial infection, produces hard galls on many kinds of trees and plants. These vary from pea-

White pine forests are often severely damaged by infections of blister rust (Cronartium), *a fungus disease that causes the formation of large galls or knots on the limbs.*

size to large growths weighing 50 pounds or more. On some trees, this disease causes the growth of the so-called "witches'-brooms," clustered masses of twigs or branches.

Often, in oak forests, enormous galls are seen on the limbs or trunks of the trees. Such strange, abnormal growths result from infection by viruses. Since the grain of the wood inside these great galls is twisted and coiled, lumber or veneer cut from them is very beautiful and much in demand by manufacturers of fine furniture.

Thus, since ancient times, plant galls have attracted attention in one way or another and even, in some cases, been of commercial or medicinal value. Since the true cause of gall forma-

Crown gall, a bacterial disease, causes the formation of large galls on the stems and roots of various plants and trees. The plants may be damaged. The organism responsible is Agrobacterium tumefaciens.

tion was but little understood it is not at all surprising to find that they have often been surrounded by superstitious beliefs. In the Middle Ages they were thought to be supernatural growths. It is difficult for us who live in more enlightened times to understand how much faith people once placed in galls as a means of foretelling future events. In order to determine what the coming year would bring, it was merely necessary to cut open a gall and study its contents. If the gall contained the larval wasp, famine was betokened for the coming year; if a "fly"—actually the tiny wasp—was present, there would be war; but if a spider was found inside the gall, the year would certainly bring pestilence. No doubt spiders often hid inside old

Galls of enormous size are frequently seen on the trunks of forest trees, especially hardwoods. This specimen on an oak tree, produced by a virus infection, was three feet in diameter.

galls, so it is not surprising that they were frequently found there. Remember that those were days of ignorance and unrest and whatever evil things the galls foretold had an excellent chance of coming true. Thus, the forecasts were more often correct than wrong. But ancient superstitions die slowly, so it is not surprising to find that, even in recent times, the contents of galls have been examined for their ability to foretell the future. The newer version of the ancient superstition goes this way: If an oak gall is cut open in the fall, one of three things is apt to be found; a fly (wasp) denotes want, a worm (larval wasp) denotes prosperity, while a spider signifies death.

While galls of one kind or another have, in the past, been found useful to man as sources of various things, it is possible that studies of their physiology may one day give us clues to the way in which animal tumors and cancers are formed. This is because there appears to be a similarity between the irregular or asymmetrical *mitosis* (cell division) of plant gall growth and cancer and tumor formation in animals. This is not to imply that plant galls are cancerous growths, yet there are certain similarities as well as certain differences. The chief difference lies in the fact that a gall develops only as a result of a continuous supply of the stimulating substance secreted by the insect or other gall-forming plant or animal. Animal tumors and cancers apparently need no such agency.

105

*Insects not only feed upon leaves but construct shelters of them as well. Here, a leaf-rolling cricket (*Camptonotus carolinensis*) "sews" a leaf into a daytime shelter. At night this unusual cricket leaves its leaf shelter to hunt for plant lice upon which it feeds.*

7

MINERS IN LEAVES

The insect world is a world of miniatures, a strange Lilliputian realm where smallness is the rule. Yet, among the insects there is tremendous variation in size between the largest and the smallest. If we compare them to the mammal clan, we find that the largest mammal is the blue whale weighing as much as a hundred tons. By contrast, the smallest mammal is the shrew, tipping the scales at about an ounce. Thus, the blue whale, probably the largest creature the world has ever known, weighs approximately three million times as much as the shrew.

Insects, by contrast, are all small, yet between the largest and the smallest insect, the range in size is probably even greater than that between the shrew and the whale. The largest insect living today is the Atlas moth of India with a wing spread of seventeen inches. At the opposite end of the scale is the fairy-fly, a minute wasp, measuring but one-hundredth of an inch across its fringed wings. The fairy-fly is even smaller than some single-celled protozoa.

Insects, being small, have been able to adapt themselves to life in places where larger creatures could not exist. Among the smallest of the insects are the leaf miners that tunnel along between the upper and lower surfaces of leaves that are almost as thin as this page.

Leaves are remarkable structures. Each spring a tree unfolds a new set of leaves, each one complete in every detail and perfectly fitted to carry out its function of food manufacture. The leaves are held up to the sun, the source of the energy that enables them to do their work. A leaf may look like a fragment of paper, yet within it are layers of cells, as well as many veins, some of which carry water and minerals from the roots while others carry manufactured sugars and other foods away to nourish the growing tree. As long as it lives a tree never stops growing.

Spiders, too, build leaf shelters. This grass blade has been cleverly formed into a box-like cell.

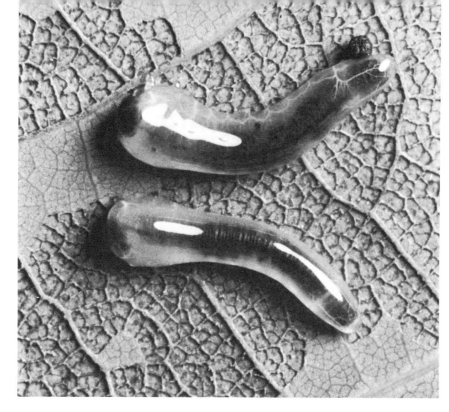

Leaves constitute the food of thousands of different insects. Here, two insect larvae feed upon the surface tissues of a tree leaf.

By summer's end the leaves are worn out and ragged from the attacks of leaf-eating insects and frayed by winds. The tree usually drops them, one by one, and they fall to the ground and decay, adding their organic matter to the soil. In time, this organic matter will be reabsorbed by the tree's roots and transformed into the leaves of another spring.

Leaves, paper-thin as they are, are very nutritious and so are fed upon by numerous insects. Also, they may be formed into snug shelters to protect insects from weather and enemies. Each dawn the leaf-rolling cricket rolls itself in a leaf and "sews" the edges together with silk. Within this protective envelope the cricket is safe from sharp-eyed birds. Leaf-rolling caterpillars, too, have similar habits. The gall-making insects, as we have already seen, secrete chemical substances into leaves, causing

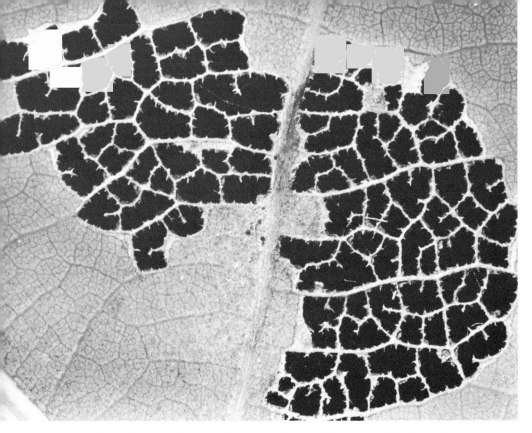

Some insects devour the entire leaf, others eat only the softer portions, leaving the tough veins. Here is the end result of such a leaf-skeletonizer.

them to produce special dwelling places well stocked with food. By contrast, the leaf miners live within the leaf, feeding upon the tissues but causing no changes except for the destruction of some of its cells. Here, protected by the relatively tough epidermis covering both upper and lower surfaces, the leaf miners excavate their tunnels, feeding and growing as they go and creating characteristic patterns that remain as clues to their identities.

Since the mines excavated by these insects are fairly constant for each kind of miner, the tunnels they make in leaves are, in a way, their signatures or trade marks. Because the epidermis or "skin" of a leaf is transparent, the excavations beneath it are quite conspicuous and may be classified as either *blotch* mines

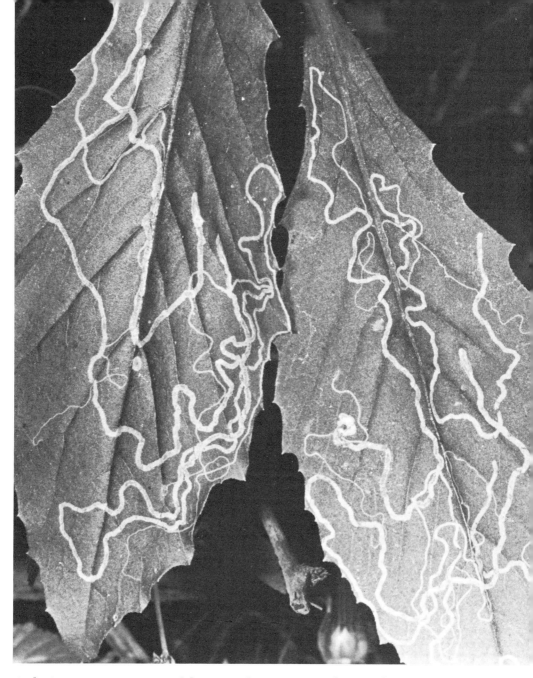

As leaf mining insects tunnel between the surfaces of leaves, they leave
meandering trails which become wider as the insects gradually increase in
size. Try to trace the paths of the various insect larvae from the time they
hatched from eggs to the completion of their wanderings through the leaves.

or as *linear* mines. Blotch mines are formed when the insect feeds in one area, creating an irregular or circular patch. Linear mines, by contrast, result when the insects mine through the tissues following either straight or winding courses. If the mine wanders about through the leaf, it is called a *serpentine* (snake-like) mine. These latter are the most attractive and the most interesting. Sometimes they are confined to one portion of the leaf; in other cases they meander about through the entire leaf, often from base to tip and from one side to the other. Frequently, too, a mine may begin as a linear mine and end in a blotch, or a serpentine mine may cross and recross itself. The variations of the patterns are almost endless.

If we study a cross-section of a leaf under a microscope we find that it is made up of several layers of cells. Covering both upper and lower surfaces is the *cuticle* or thin, transparent "skin." Just inside the cuticle of both upper and lower surfaces are layers of *epidermal* cells. These, too, are transparent and allow the sunlight to penetrate into the leaf. Beneath the upper

Some mining insects feed in small areas of a leaf, making blotch *mines.*

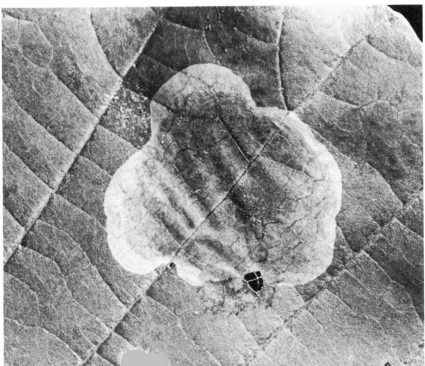

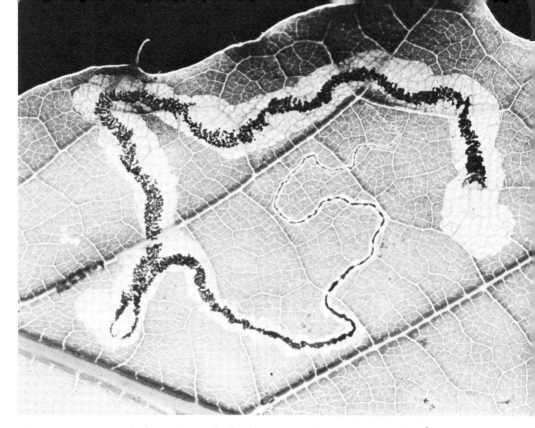

Other miners tunnel about through the leaves creating serpentine (snake-like) mines. In this close-up, the larval insect hatched from an egg laid near one of the larger veins and meandered about across the leaf, gradually increasing the width of its mine as it grew larger. Then mature, the larval insect left the leaf (right) and dropped to the ground to pupate. The dark streak consists of waste material or frass.

epidermis lies a zone of closely packed cells placed side by side. This is the *palisade* layer which usually fills about half of the space between the leaf surfaces. Just below this is a zone of loosely packed cells called the *spongy* layer. Between these cells there are air spaces, the air entering and leaving through breathing pores or *stomates* in the lower surface of the leaf.

Even though a leaf is very thin, leaf-mining insects do not always occupy the entire space between its surfaces. Some kinds tunnel only through the palisade layer and, as a result, their mines can only be seen from above. These are called *upper*

Here, a leaf miner hatched from an egg near the lower edge of a wild blackberry leaf and tunneled upward. Near the base of the leaf it changed its direction and worked downward to a point near where it began. At the large end of its mine, it transformed into the pupal stage (dark blotch).

surface mines. Other miners feed only in the spongy layer and their mines are only visible from below. These are called *lower surface* mines. Often a leaf is found to be occupied by leaf miners of both types, their mines crossing and recrossing, one above the other. On the other hand, some miners cut away all the cells between the upper and lower surfaces. Such insects are called *full-depth* miners and their mines are visible from above and below.

Leaf mines are always the work of larval insects, either flies, sawflies, beetles, or moths. These are the same insect groups to which the gall makers belong and the gall makers, it is believed, were originally leaf miners. It is but a short step from tunneling through a leaf to secreting something into the leaf, causing it to produce a gall. The gall-making habit has the advantage that the insect is no longer forced to tunnel about where enemies

These drawings show greatly enlarged cross-sections of three leaves. Top: An upper surface leaf miner tunnels through the palisade cell layer. Center: Another miner tunnels through the spongy cell layer, creating a lower surface mine. Bottom: A caterpillar excavating a full-depth mine.

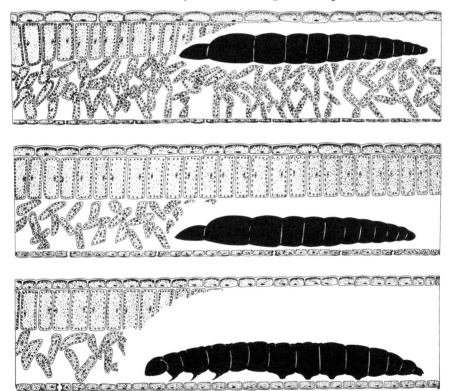

may see it. As a matter of fact, the boxwood leaf miner (*Monar-thropalpus buxi*), a midge fly larva, tunnels through the leaf in the usual manner of leaf miners, but in addition to its tunneling activities, this larva secretes something that causes the formation of a leaf blister or blister gall within which it lives. Another gall fly (*Agromyza laterella*) produces galls (green leaf galls) on young iris leaves, but mines in older iris leaves. Thus, the habits of some leaf miners may vary from one to the other.

The insect larvae that mine in leaves have become specially adapted to the lives they live. Usually their bodies are flattened and their legs are often absent or reduced in size. In many cases their heads are wedge-shaped with the mouthparts extending forward. Naturally they cannot move about as freely as ordinary leaf-eating insects and so their feeding habits are different.

It is possible to watch one of these minute insects as it feeds within a leaf. Hold the leaf toward a strong light and watch the

One of the most common leaf miners is the nasturtium miner (Agromyza pusilla), *a fly larva that leaves serpentine trails across the leaves.*

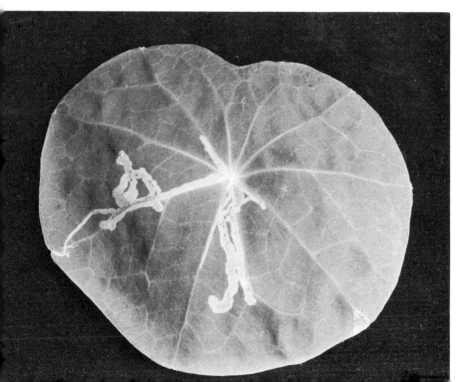

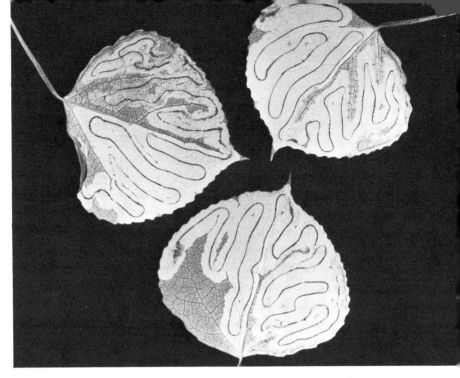

The leaves of western quaking aspens often show the characteristic mines of moth larvae (Phyllocnistis populiella). *They tunnel in the lower surfaces of the leaves, giving them a silvery appearance.*

insect through a hand lens. If it is a beetle larva, it thrusts its head in and out of its thorax each time it takes a bite. Within the confined space where it lives, it cannot easily move its entire body. It opens its jaws, pushes its head forward and bites into the leaf tissue, then withdraws its head as it swallows the food. This is repeated again and again as it feeds.

Moth larvae, on the other hand, have slightly different feeding habits; they usually live upon the fluid sap that flows out when the cells are cut open. In feeding, the larva moves its head from side to side as its saw-edged mandibles shear away the walls of the cells, allowing the liquid food to flow into its mouth. Fly larvae, by contrast, lie on their sides and swing their mouthparts up and down as they cut their way through the leaf.

As might be suspected, an insect that tunnels through a leaf is faced with the problem of waste disposal. Different insects have solved this problem in different ways. Many, perhaps most, insects eject their waste into the tunnels behind them, leaving dark streaks in the transparent mines. This waste material is called *frass*. Some miners make openings in the leaves out of which they eject their frass. The locust leaf miner (*Parectopa robiniella*), a moth larva, mines through the palisade layer but maintains a storage place for its frass in the lower portion of the leaf, the cellar, so to speak.

Some miners can be identified by the manner in which they dispose of their frass. In the case of the peach leaf miner (*Phytomyza nigritella*), the frass is arranged in a distinct line of spots. In the trumpet miner of apple leaves (*Tischeria malifoliella*), it is deposited in crossband patterns.

Not only do mining insects excavate their tunnels through leaves but beneath the skins of fruits as well. The surfaces of apples often contain the meandering mines of tiny caterpillars (*Marmara pomonella*).

One of the more interesting leaf miners is the maple casebearer (*Paraclemensia acerifoliella*). This miner is the larval stage of a small moth that lays its eggs on the leaves of sugar maples. When one of these eggs hatches, the larva bores into the leaf and begins its mining operations, continuing to do so for about ten days. At this time it is hardly one-sixteenth of an inch in length and greenish in color. The mine it has created in the leaf is oval in shape and the little caterpillar now makes oval cuts in the upper and lower surfaces of the leaf, making the lower section slightly larger than the upper one. It next "sews" the edges of the two sections together with silk. The larva is now enclosed in an oval case and it then pushes the front part of its body out and drags the case onto the surface of the leaf, at the same time flipping the case over so that the larger section is on

118

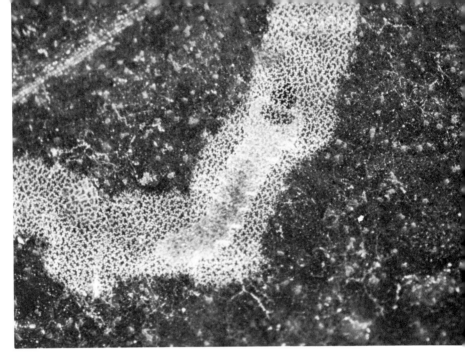

In this extreme close-up, a minute caterpillar is shown in its tunnel beneath the upper, semi-transparent surface of a smilax leaf. Notice the unusual cell forms in the leaf surface.

Here, the thin transparent tissues of the leaf have been stripped off, revealing the minute leaf-mining caterpillar which is 1/16 of an inch long.

When mature, some leaf miners pupate within their mines; others leave them and drop to the ground. In this close-up, a tiny leaf-mining caterpillar has changed into its pupal stage and pushed out of the leaf. The adult moth has already emerged.

top. It is now able to drag its "house" about, looking much like a tiny turtle in its shell. Protected by this case, the larva crawls about over the leaf, reaching out now and then to feed upon the green tissues. As might be expected, the case soon becomes too small and the larva is forced to enlarge it, a task that it does in a very clever manner. First, it fastens the case down to the leaf with silken strands extending out from its edges and then cuts a slit completely around its old case, but somewhat larger. The old case, with the larva inside, is now held in place by the silk strands attached to its edges. The little insect, now in its slightly larger case, may do one of two things: it may elect to drag its case out upon the upper surface of the leaf, making it necessary to flip the case over so that the larger leaf section is on top, or it may drag the case upon the lower surface of the leaf. If the latter step is taken, the case does not have to be flipped over.

It is a rather tricky maneuver to cut the silken strands holding the case in place, while at the same time preventing it from falling to the ground. One authority has summed the matter up in this way, "It is somewhat like sawing off a limb of a tree while seated on it, and yet not getting a tumble."

In any event, these little caterpillars have learned how to do it and the process of case enlargement must be repeated several times before they reach maturity. The caterpillar pupates within its case, having attached it to the sugar maple leaf with silk. The leaf, of course, eventually falls to the ground and here the pupa passes the winter. In late spring the moth that emerges is half an inch across its spread wings which are brilliant steel-blue with violet reflections. There is a tuft of orange-yellow hairs on the little moth's head.

There is considerable variation in the life histories of the leaf miners; some kinds spend only short portions of their larval lives as miners, eventually leaving the security of the mines to feed on the outsides of the leaves. Others continue to mine within the leaves until ready to transform into pupae. Still others transform into pupae while still in their mines and the adult, winged insects then push out of the leaf and fly away. In some miners, especially the larvae of moths, the pupal cases push out through the leaf surface and the winged adult then emerges. Other miners, when full grown, drop to the ground where they burrow in and pupate, spending the winter protected from both enemies and cold.

All mining insects are naturally of small size and the moths, especially, are frequently very beautiful. Because of their minute size, they are usually known as micro-lepidoptera. The insect order Lepidoptera, as you may know, includes both moths and butterflies. Many of the tiny leaf-mining moths are marked with silver, gold, white, and black.

Adult leaf miners usually lay their eggs either on or in the

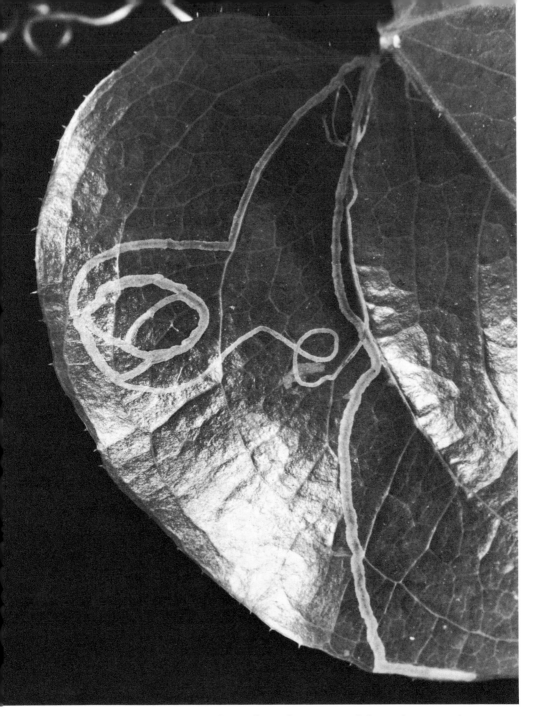

See if you can trace the path of this tiny moth larva (Marmara) *as it tunneled in a smilax leaf.*

surface of the leaf. The young may break out of the eggs and then bore into the leaf or they may bore directly down into the leaf at the points where the eggs are attached.

It might seem that the leaf miners, protected as they are within the leaves, would be safe from most enemies. Probably this was true long ago when they first took up the mining habit, but this is no longer so. Once their enemies found out about them and how to gain entrance to their tunnels, they were worse off than before. This is because leaf miners have no means of escape. Many parasites, including tiny wasps, infest them. Predaceous bugs pierce their bodies through the thin cuticle of the leaf and siphon out their blood. Birds of many kinds find and eat them. These include warblers, creepers, nuthatches, and sparrows. In addition, a number of "guests" move in and live with them in their tunnels, much to the sorrow of their hosts.

INDEX

Page numbers in **boldface** are those on which illustrations appear

126

INDEX TO PHOTOGRAPHS OF GALLS
ACCORDING TO HOST PLANTS